Against All Odds...BUT GOD!

An Account of the Activities
of the first
Fifty Years
of the
Christian Chiropractors Association

by Glenn M. Hultgren, D.C.

Copyright © 2003
Glenn M. Hultgren and the
Christian Chiropractors Association

Published by:
        Christian Chiropractors Association, Inc.
        P.O. Box 9715
        Fort Collins, CO 80525

In conjunction with:
        The Association for the History of Chiropractic
        1000 Brady Street
        Davenport, Iowa 52803

Library of Congress
Cataloging-in-Publication Data Control number 2003104272
Hultgren, Glenn M. 1932-
"Against All Odds ... BUT God!"

Includes Bibliographical references and index.

ISBN 0-9659131-5-5

Acknowledgements and Thank You

To my daughter, Bonnie Jeffers (M.A.) for her editing and her husband James (Ph.D.) for his counsel and advice.

To my son, Robert, for his typesetting, layout and cover design work.

To my wife, MaryLou, and the many others who gave encouragement.

To Joseph C. Keating, Jr., (Ph.D.), chiropractic historian, who challenged me to write this account in the first place.

                                              Thanks to all,
                                            Glenn M. Hultgren
                                               1913 Sequoia
                                        Fort Collins, Colorado
                                             March 30, 2003

Foreword

In reviewing Dr. Hultgren's, Against All Odds ... BUT GOD! I was reminded of when I accepted the invitation from Rev. Charles Swindoll to write the volume Salvation in the Swindoll Leadership Library. My first goal was to do an exhaustive study of every use of the words *"save"* and *"salvation"* in the Bible. What a revelation that was! In contrast to the current tendency to use the words almost exclusively of deliverance in a spiritual sense *(i.e., justification)*, the scripture has a strong emphasis on the physical deliverance. And often the physical deliverance leads to the spiritual deliverance *(justification, sanctification, and glorification)*.

Actually, the word salvation has its roots in the Hebrew word *"to be wide or roomy"* in contrast to *"narrow or restricted."* In other words, *"room to breathe."* Thus, words such as liberation, emancipation, preservation, protection, and security grow out of it. It refers to delivering a person or group of people from distress or danger, from a *"restricted"* condition in which they are unable to help themselves.

I recall David's cry of distress to the Lord:
> *"Have mercy on me, O Lord, for I am weak,*
> *O Lord, heal me, for my bones are troubled;*
> *But You, O Lord - how long?*
> *Return, O Lord, deliver me!*
> *Oh, save me for Your mercies' sake,*
> *For in death there is no remembrance of You;*
> *In the grave who will give You thanks?*
> *I am weary with my groaning;*
> *All night I make my bed swim;*
> *I drench my couch with my tears."* (Psalms 6:2-6)

And David continues and I am sure many can identify with him.

The New Testament work broadens the idea of rescue of deliverance to include recovery, safety, and preservation. There is a progression in these concepts: **(a)** rescue from imminent and life-threatening danger to **(b)** a place of safety and security and **(c)** a position of wholeness and soundness. The narrowness and restriction created by danger and distress is replaced by the *"breadth"* of liberation in salvation.

The central, dramatic act of salvation in the Old Testament - the crossing of the Red Sea on dry land by the nation of Israel - is climaxed by Moses with these words: *"So the Lord saved (emphasis mine) Israel that day out of the hand of the Egyptians, and Israel saw the Egyptians dead on the seashore. Thus Israel saw the great work which the Lord had done in Egypt; so the people feared the Lord, and believed (emphasis mine) the Lord and His servant Moses"* (Exodus 14:30-31). *(The word "believed" here translates the same word used of Abraham in Genesis 15:6: "And he believed in the Lord, and He accounted it to him for righteousness.")* Think of it! The physical deliverance of a nation was the event that God used to lead to the spiritual deliverance of that nation.

In like fashion, the ministry of Jesus Christ — the apex of revelation — regularly combined the therapy of physical healing with spiritual healing. He had compassion for those in distress. Using the problem of their temporal pain and distress, He led people to the ultimate solution of eternal deliverance and wholeness. By meeting the need of their immediate pain, He led them to reception of a spiritual deliverance that would one day bring final deliverance. Looking to that day, the aged Apostle John exulted: *"And God will wipe away every tear from their eyes; there shall be no more death, nor sorrow, nor crying. There shall be no more pain, for the former things have passed away."* (Rev. 21:4)

Through my personal acquaintance over the past couple of decades with the author of Against All Odds ... BUT GOD!, Dr. Glenn M. Hultgren and the Christian Chiropractors Association, it has been my privilege to be invited several times to serve as their Bible teacher at their annual conventions. The highlight of those conventions was listening to the doctors bring reports of how God enabled them, often in very difficult and extremely needy situations, to bring together the full spectrum of the word salvation. It started with their HANDS touching hurting bodies but often concluded with a change of mind and heart that brought true wholeness *(i.e., "room to breathe")*. Without giving the theological digest that I have briefly given, they DID good theology by deed and word. Dr.

Hultgren's recounting of fifty years of living it with them will bring rejoicing to your heart as well as motivation to carry on this great mission of full-orbed salvation by the Christian Chiropractors Association.

Rejoicing in the matchless grace of Christ through His servants,

Earl D. Radmacher, M.A., Th.D.
President Emeritus and Professor of
Systemic Theology Emeritus
Western Conservative Baptist Seminary
Portland, Oregon

Table of Contents

Part I: Missionary Doctors of Chiropractic Who Used their Professional Training on the Mission Field

Part II: Bi-Vocational Doctors of Chiropractic Who Supported their Mission Activity through their Professional Practice

Part III: Christian Missionaries Who were Doctors of Chiropractic

Part IV: Student Projects

Part V: Short-Term Missions

Introduction

Every committed Christian has a desire to have a part in fulfilling the commandment of Christ in His Great Commission, *"Go therefore and make disciples of all the nations, baptizing them in the name of the Father and the Son and the Holy Spirit."* (Matt. 28:19) Regardless of the calling we have in life, regardless of our education, training, social status, geographical location, or any other variable, we must work toward fulfilling this command. Nowhere does Scripture say that only one social classification, one nation, one profession, or one type of education equips us to win others for Christ. Paul said, *"I have become all things to all men, that I may by all means save some."* (I Cor, 9:22) With the Word of God as our guide, we are to use the education and talent we have been given for His glory.

This is not to suggest that education, be it Bible college, secular college, or seminary, is to be criticized. Rather, it is to be considered an extreme privilege. Nonetheless, such education alone should not be the supreme qualification for carrying out the Great Commission. Even the best education without a calling and blessing from the Lord will yield no fruit. We need to realize that the exclusive right to fulfillment of the Great Commission does not depend on education alone. Many times we have read of an uneducated tribal native who is unable to even read the tracts that he is using, yet winning souls to Christ.

I am reminded of a Gideon Bible that was given to a school child in Central America. He took it home and threw it on the kitchen table. After dinner gravy covered it, the family dog grabbed the Bible for the sake of the gravy and took off running. A neighbor saw the dog with something in its mouth and threw a rock forcing the dog to drop his prize. The neighbor retrieved the Bible, read it, realized his need for the Savior, and gave his heart to the Lord.

If a dog can deliver the Word of God to a lost, needy soul who is seeking God, surely we must realize that our expensive church buildings, many college degrees, and detailed planning and programs are not the only way to reach the lost for Christ.

The mission accounts in this book are meant to illustrate that God can and does use people of many different talents and abilities to accomplish His purpose. Churches, mission societies, and society in general often look only at the educational qualifications that are "approved" by the secular world. Fortunately, God does not live by man's standards.

In the 1950s, doctors of chiropractic were considered to have an inferior education and to be unfit for missionary service except as technicians or helpers in dispensaries. They were not accepted on par with medical doctors in health ministries on mission fields around the world. In the years since, in dozens of fields around the world, missionaries of the Christian Chiropractors Association have proven this perception to be wrong.

It has long been known that the most effective way to bring souls to the hearing of the Word of God and to meet their spiritual needs was to first provide for their physical needs. Therefore, missionaries have used many ways to meet these needs. In its early years, the American church was responsible for building the first schools and colleges, the first hospitals and shelters for the homeless, the alcoholic, the pregnant teen, and the downtrodden.

On foreign fields too, schools and medical services were—and still are—being established to serve the great physical needs around the world. Missionaries find this helps them gain the good will of the people, serve a need, and also introduce the gospel of Jesus Christ. Some unique services have included providing food and garden seed for people in famine areas; installing pumps, wells, and windmills in drought-stricken areas; and providing literature, educational, and printing services in underdeveloped areas. As Paul said, *"that I may by all means save some."* (I Cor. 9:22)

Prior to World War II, no one considered any medical services other than that of the medical physician. But as chiropractic became more accepted in America and patients began to see that health benefits could be realized without drugs or surgery in many cases, it seemed only logical that chiropractic should be included on the mission field.

After all, did not the chiropractor heal with just his hands? Was this not following a Biblical example? Furthermore, the chiropractor did not need a constant supply of drugs and medications; his service was not stopped when a shipment of supplies did not arrive. The chiropractor's hands were his only tools! Also some missionaries noted that many tribal people were afraid of the sharp needles of the medical doctors; the chiropractor's gentle hands were far more readily accepted.

For example, shortly after World War II, 54-year-old Dr. Don Phibbs of Vancouver, British Columbia, went to Japan as a bi-vocational missionary. He finally returned to his home in Canada 30 years later at age 84. In 1959 Dr. Don's sister, Dr. Myrtle Belle Phibbs Baker, joined his ministry. Dr. Baker's husband had been killed in World War I after only one and a half years of marriage. After first entering the nursing profession, Dr. Baker decided to become a chiropractor and entered Palmer School of Chiropractic. She graduated in 1925 and practiced in Canada for 32 years before setting up a home office in a semi-urban area northeast of Tokyo.

The Christian Chiropractors Association never became acquainted with Dr. Phibbs or Dr. Baker, and they did not receive any aid from the C.C.A. But they were early examples of bi-professional ministry teaching the Bible at every opportunity and using their chiropractic care to reach out to people in need.

The middle of the 20th century witnessed a terrific conflict between the medical and chiropractic professions. No North American mission society would send a chiropractor unless he provided some service other than chiropractic. To do so would bring swift reprisal from medical organizations; furthermore, medical doctors would be discouraged from serving under that mission board.

It is not the purpose of this book to reiterate all of those conflicts, and it is safe to say there was reason for blame on both sides. But for the large part, when the two professions worked together on the mission field, partisan politics generally disappeared. If nothing else, Christian doctors of both professions found that they could work together for the basic good of the patients they served on the field, provided the North American medical associations were not told about it.

I will never forget an experience I had in 1968 on a mission trip in Dembi Dollo, Ethiopia. Dr. Rasmusson, the mission doctor, asked if I wanted to make the morning rounds with him at the base hospital. He, along with one other doctor and two nurses, had about 48 bed patients.

Our first stop was the maternity ward where he had delivered a baby with instruments the night before. The baby was paralyzed on one side of its body—face, arm, and leg. Dr. Rasmusson and his staff checked the baby over and did not know what could be done for it other than to hope it would get better with time. I asked Dr. Rasmusson if I could examine the baby and realized right away that the neck had been twisted, and there was a severe subluxation of the first cervical vertebra.

I told Dr. Rasmusson, "If this were my patient, this is what I would do"—and I gave the baby a quick adjustment of the misaligned vertebra. It was one of those one-in-a-lifetime events when you see everything happen at once: the doctors and staff stood there in amazement as the baby instantly began to move both arms and legs and appeared to be perfectly normal. From that point on, Dr. Rasmusson gave me permission to adjust any and all of the patients in his hospital. However, of all the patients he had—some with infections, leukemia, stab wounds, broken bones—there was not one other patient that I wanted to adjust.

When we left the hospital, Dr. Rasmusson said, "I wish we could work together like this back home!" I said, "yes, I wish we could too, and so do many of our patients." That was over thirty years ago; working together was not possible at that time at home, but there were windows of opportunity on the mission field.

By 1953 at least five doctors of chiropractic were serving the Lord overseas. They had all been appointed to mission service for some purpose other than health care. They were not with the same mission society or in the same field, but each one did what he or she was called to do—and also did some chiropractic on the side. The time was right to form a Christian Chiropractors Association to provide home support for chiropractors on foreign mission fields.

At that time, no mission society or organization would provide chiropractic equipment, and generally the most these doctors had was a portable adjusting table which could be folded up and taken from place to place. Some tell of giving adjustments on the floor, on logs in the jungle, and on makeshift cots and tables.

In this book I hope to show that God can and will use dedicated people— with or without expensive equipment—and that when He decides to use a man or woman, He will bless that work. Regardless of opposition from other men and organizations, God's plan will go forth. Today we see that the seeds planted forty, fifty, and sixty years ago by our first missionary chiropractors have brought forth tremendous fruit. Thousands have heard the gospel while a chiropractor is offering health services without drugs or surgery. Hundreds of churches have been started in areas where a chiropractic clinic was first established.

While forty years ago no mission society would allow a doctor of chiropractic to be a missionary chiropractor, now many societies are recruiting and commissioning doctors of chiropractic. Today missionaries all over the world are asking for a resident chiropractor to serve with them, if for no other purpose than to serve the health needs of the missionaries and their families. But many also know that a doctor of chiropractic can draw more people to a clinic, can treat more patients in less time with less expense, and can provide greater satisfaction to the patients than any other health service.

Hands

Your hands are made like His, and so
Be careful in the things they do.
Let them be quick to lift the weak,
Let them be kind and soft and strong.
May they be swift to heal the sick,
To ease a load ... to right a wrong.
Your hands are made like His. Beware!
They hold the weight of no man's pain,
Who asked their aid to help him bare
His suffering ... and asked in vain.
He made the deaf to hear ... the lame
To walk ... the blind to see,
Until one day the fools they came
And nailed His hands upon a tree.
Our hands are like His hands. As wings
Let them caress all living things ...
Lest He look down on earth, and see
What things are wrought beneath the sun
By us, His images ... and be
Ashamed of what His hands have done.

(Author Unknown)

The Founding

It was 1951. Palmer School of Chiropractic in Davenport, Iowa, had no Campus Crusade for Christ or Navigators. Chiropractic student Frank Torok saw a need for some type of Christian witness on this growing campus and formed the Christian Student Fellowship Club for early morning Bible study and prayer.

Franklin Torok, D.C.

Frank soon affiliated with InterVarsity Christian Fellowship (I.V.C.F.), and the I.V.C.F. representative would occasionally visit the Christian students. It is ironic that this early affiliation should be with I.V.C.F., for over the years this organization has been one of the most vociferous and vitriolic opponents of chiropractic. I.V.C.F. has published many articles critical of chiropractic and has not encouraged Christian students in the various chiropractic colleges. At Palmer in those early days, however, the representatives from I.V.C.F. were supportive and helpful.

As far as is known, this was the first Christian outreach within the chiropractic profession. I am sure that Frank and the others involved at that time had no idea of how far their little Bible study group would reach in its impact on the world for Christ.

Dr. Frank Torok graduated from Palmer in 1953 and practiced chiropractic in Jackson, Kentucky, for many years. Frank was later ordained as a minister in the Assemblies of God Church and assisted in pastoring a church for many years. Frank was an outstanding Christian, a good witness for the Lord Jesus Christ and an able soul winner.

Capturing a Vision

From the very earliest years, Palmer School and its founder and president, Dr. B. J. Palmer, had an annual homecoming called Lyceum. Each August a big circus tent was erected on the school parking lot to accommodate the crowds. Chiropractors from all over North America would return to Davenport for inspiration from Dr. B.J., for fellowship with old classmates, and for instruction in new ideas.

Dr. B.J. invited Dr. Robert N. Thompson to speak "in the tent" at the 1953 Lyceum. Dr. Thompson had graduated from Palmer School in 1939 and was serving as a missionary in charge of a leprosarium in Ethiopia. (More on Drs. Robert and Hazel Thompson in later chapters.) The seven- to eight- thousand Lyceum attendees, heard Dr. Thompson, an excellent speaker with a very charismatic and persuasive manner, tell of the position he had been offered with the Sudan Interior Mission in southern Ethiopia.

He outlined his plan for and dream of a research center for chiropractic service to leper patients. Never before had a chiropractor had an opportunity to work with leprosy and other tropical diseases. The potential for opening up an entirely new field of service for chiropractic care challenged the audience. But Dr. Thompson stated it would take money to buy equipment—chiropractic equipment, x-ray equipment, and laboratory equipment.

In the audience was Dr. Mattie Carswell Stephens of Thomaston, Georgia. Dr. Mattie, a classmate of Mrs. Robert Thompson (Dr. Hazel Kurth Thompson), had followed the Thompsons' careers since they were in school. She had supported them as missionaries in Ethiopia and was excited about the opportunities this new assignment presented.

Dr. Frank Torok had graduated, so Dr. Mattie contacted the new president of the I.V.C.F. student group at Palmer—me. I shall never forget Dr. Mattie saying, "WE have got to do something!"

"Mattie what to do you mean WE? I am only a student and you are a single, older woman (She was about 60 years old at the time). This project is going to take a lot more than you and I are going to be able to do!"

Well, there was no stopping Dr. Mattie.   *Dr. Mattie Carswell Stephens*

The next morning she came running across the campus and said, "The Lord spoke to me last night and He gave me this verse: *'Call unto me, and I will answer thee, and show thee great and mighty things which thou knowest not.'*(Jer. 33:3) Don't you see? God is in this thing! He wants us to do something and we dare not let Him down—we can't stop now!"

"But Mattie what can WE do?" Well I learned never to underestimate the power of a committed woman when God tells her do to something! So Dr. Mattie and I sat on a bench there on the Palmer campus and prayed. We prayed for God's will in this matter and whether we were supposed to have a part in it. We prayed for the Thompsons. And we prayed that God would give us wisdom! It was against all odds...but God!

In the meantime, The International Chiropractors Association (I.C.A.) told Dr. Thompson that they would promote his project in their journal *(The International Review of Chiropractic)* and help raise funds for the equipment that he needed. Dr. Lyle Sherman was selected chairman of the project with Dr. Mattie Stephens as vice chairperson. Hugh Chance of the I.C.A. agreed to act as legal counsel.

Dr. Robert Thompson and Dr. Lyle Sherman

Dr. Mattie asked both Drs. Robert and Hazel Thompson for their suggestions on the project. She also told them about our conversation. Dr. Robert Thompson was probably more of a visionary than any of us in seeing this leading to the formation of a Christian chiropractors association. He asked if I could help raise funds from the Palmer students and staff and if Dr. Mattie could contact all of the Christian doctors of chiropractic that she knew. At this time the three of us decided that we really needed a CHRISTIAN CHIROPRACTORS ASSOCIATION!

Forming an Association

When Lyceum was over, we each went our separate ways but agreed to stay in touch. Funds began coming in from all over the profession. Our student chapter began publicizing the project and asking for support.

Dr. Mattie contacted Palmer graduates such as Dr. Frank Torok, Dr. Lou Sage of Sunnyvale, California, Dr. Harry Kalsbeek of Castro Valley, California, Dr. Luther Frondal of Eau Claire, Wisconsin, and others to help built a list of Christian supporters. The I.C.A. also shared the list of its donors who were contributing to the project. We asked each one to give us names of other Christians in the profession. Soon our list began to grow–twenty or twenty-five students plus ten, then twenty, then thirty doctors.

It really might be possible to have an association of Christian chiropractors. But who was I to start that? I was only a student and had almost two years left in school! I went to a very dear older member in the church I attended in Davenport, Perry Hedberg. Mr. Hedberg was a deacon at Grandview Baptist Church, but he also was a Gideon! From what I knew, Gideons was an organization with many of the same ideals, standards, and goals that we envisioned for a Christian chiropractors association.

I asked Mr. Hedberg for a copy of the Gideons' by-laws and studied it for several days. Indeed the organization as set forth in these by-laws was very much like the organization that we had in mind. The purpose for both organizations was to win souls, but the organization I was trying to start was going to do it through the profession of chiropractic and not by distributing God's Word as the Gideons did.

At that time we adopted the following objectives:

1. To band together in Christian fellowship professional chiropractors and to encourage them in proclaiming Christ at every opportunity and to bear a living testimony for Christ in all professional, business and personal relationships;

2. To gain recognition on mission boards for chiropractors;

3. To help, financially and otherwise, our chiropractic missionaries;

4. To encourage Christian chiropractors to enter missionary service;

5. To help, financially and otherwise, deserving foreign Christians through chiropractic training;

6. To help, financially and otherwise, Christian students through chiropractic schools and colleges.

I proceeded through the Gideons' by-laws from beginning to end, page after page, word for word. I sent copies to Dr. Mattie and Dr. Thompson. They made suggestions and gave their approval. In the end, we had a constitution and by-laws which was to be the basis of the Christian Chiropractors Association.

Taking the Next Steps

In the meantime, the International Chiropractors Association received sufficient donations to purchase and ship the chiropractic, x-ray, and laboratory equipment that Dr. Thompson had requested. Our new Christian Chiropractors Association received the list of donors and screened it for prospective members. This was all accomplished between August 1953 and August 1955.

At the end of 1955, I graduated from Palmer and moved to my home state of North Dakota to set up practice in Bismarck. With my move went the "office" of the Christian Chiropractors Association. I still carried on all the business of the association, wrote the letters, maintained a bank account, sent out periodic newsletters, and tried to continue recruiting members. We established membership dues of $2.00 per year for students and $10.00 per year for doctors. Needless to say, our treasury did not build up very fast, but the only expenses were stationary, envelopes, and postage (three cent stamps).

The next obvious step was to make our organization a legal entity. I contacted Alvin C. Strutz, a Christian attorney in Bismarck who later became Chief Justice of the North Dakota Supreme Court. Mr. Strutz drew up the necessary papers to make the Christian Chiropractors Association a non-profit corporation. On July 29, 1957, we paid the attorney's fee and the State of North Dakota incorporation fee. We were a legal entity—but we were broke.

Sponsoring Ethiopian Students

About this time Dr. Thompson asked if we could sponsor two or three Ethiopian young men to attend a chiropractic college. He felt his time in Ethiopia was limited, and he wanted to leave a legacy of chiropractic in this African nation. Three young men who had been working with him in the Sheshemane Leprosarium would make good chiropractors, but they would need sponsors. We wanted to do this for Dr. Bob, but our young C.C.A. was not in any financial condition to take on that responsibility. It was against all odds...BUT GOD.

Undaunted, Dr. Thompson shared his plan with and persuaded Ethiopia's Emperor Haille Sellassie to pay the transportation costs for the men. Dr. Thompson then persuaded Dr. B.J. Palmer at Palmer School to provide full tuition scholarships for the men.

Never before had Palmer School admitted black students. Ethiopians are technically a brown race, not true African blacks like the central and western Africans, yet to Americans they look black, and this was the 1950s. It was a double miracle for Dr. B.J. not only to accept them as students but also to give them full scholarships. Could we as a Christian Chiropractors Association witness this and not agree to sponsor them? Only a miracle of God could have brought us this far; surely He would provide the help we needed if we stepped out in faith. So we agreed to provide their living expenses not having any idea where the money would come from...BUT GOD.

*Emperor Haille Sellassie of Ethiopia
with Dr. Robert Thompson*

Mulatu Baffa and Beyene Mulattu came to Palmer in October 1957 and entered the Palmer School of Chiropractic as the first native Africans to study chiropractic. Mulatu Baffa had recently married and left a wife and three-week-old daughter in Ethiopia; he did not see them again until he graduated and returned to Ethiopia in November 1960.

Funds to pay the living expenses for Mulu and Beyenne were solicited from the fledging group of members of the new Christian Chiropractors Association, and month-by-month bills were paid and enough money came in to provide for all of their expenses. (More about their future ministry in Ethiopia in later chapters.)

In October 1958 I sold my practice in Bismarck and moved to Fort Collins, Colorado. With my move, of course, was the move of the C.C.A. headquarters. At the same time, Dr. Thompson had returned from Ethiopia. Officially this was because of the health needs of some of his children. Dr. Thompson started an eighteen-month speaking tour of North America, speaking in churches and at mission conferences, chiropractic conventions, and service clubs. The C.C.A. office coordinated this tour and provided Dr. Bob with opportunities to meet Christian chiropractors and, of course, tell them of the C.C.A. This was a period of growth in our membership and a time for strengthening our organization.

Gathering at Early Conventions

In 1957 the first real C.C.A. convention was held during the Lyceum at Palmer. We met in the dissection amphitheater of the college. Dr. Glenn Stillwagon of Monongahela, Pennsylvania, was elected president. (He served in that position for fourteen years.) Dr. Mattie Stephens was elected vice-president, and I was elected executive secretary-treasurer. (I have held that office since that time.) Dr. Eugene Curtis of Grand Haven, Michigan, was our first chaplain. Our first board of directors was also elected. They were Dr. George Thompson of Calgary, Alberta (no relation of Dr. Robert N. Thompson); Dr. Franklin Torok of Jackson, Kentucky; Dr. Adolph Tronrud of Murray, Utah; and Dr. L. S. Frondal of Eau Claire, Wisconsin.

In 1958 we again held a convention during the Palmer Lyceum. This time we met at the Davenport Lend-A-Hand Club. Dr. and Mrs. J. Bridgens Johnson, a missionary chiropractor and wife from Bolivia, were our special guests. We agreed at that convention to help them obtain some chiropractic and x-ray equipment for their clinic in Bolivia. (More about that in a later chapter.)

Our 1959 convention was held in Colorado Springs, Colorado. Dr. Robert Thompson was our guest as well as chiropractic students, Beyenne Mulattu and Mulatu Baffa. Since then we have had annual conventions in various places around the United States and Canada.

Gaining National Charitable Status

By 1959 it was apparent that we needed to have recognized charitable status from the United States government. We began the process of securing a 501(c)3 charitable status under the Internal Revenue Code. We had no idea how difficult this was going to be. No chiropractic organization had ever been granted that status, and there was tremendous opposition. It was against all odds...BUT GOD.

We made several trips to the Internal Revenue Service office in Washington, D.C. Our members wrote letters to congressional representatives and senators, 45 of whom agreed to support our effort. It took over four years, but we were finally granted this status in December 1963. Ours was the first chiropractic group recognized as a charitable organization by the U. S. Internal Revenue Service. (The Kentuckiana Children Center received their status around the same time.)

By 1960 the Christian Chiropractors Association was a small, yet viable, group of very committed doctors of chiropractic making their mark for the cause of Christ through their chosen profession.

Chiropractic Missions

The Christian Chiropractors Association purposes "to go into all the world with the Gospel of Jesus Christ" and to use chiropractic to promote that message. During the first fifty years of the association, over 50 doctors of chiropractic have fulfilled that purpose with a commitment to career-long mission activity. Several hundred other doctors of chiropractic have committed time ranging from one week to one year using their chiropractic training to fulfill the Great Commission in over100 countries.

Originally, C.C.A. was to provide equipment to doctors of chiropractic who were serving in some capacity with a recognized mission society. None of the five chiropractors on the field at the time C.C.A. began were using their chiropractic training on the mission field and none had any chiropractic equipment.

Over the years several situations developed.

1. Some missionary doctors of chiropractic made their outreach more effective using C.C.A.-provided chiropractic equipment.

2. Some missionary doctors of chiropractic chose to use their professional training on the mission field only in a very limited way and secondary to their primary responsibilities.

3. Some doctors of chiropractic developed commercial practices in third world countries and did only a limited amount of missions activity in their free time.

4. And some doctors of chiropractic developed what could be called bi-vocational practices using a commercial chiropractic practice to support themselves and their mission activity. They planted and pastored churches and developed evangelistic programs.

The Christian Chiropractors Association met the individual needs of these doctors in a variety of ways. All received our prayers and moral support, and some received money or equipment.

These doctors of chiropractic exemplified dedication in doing their duty as missionaries. In the following pages you will read the stories behind these quotes:

"The bandit fired his gun at me through the window and it struck me in the left eye. Blood was flowing all over my face. I knew I was going to die..."

"Some Communist youth gangs took all of my possessions and that of my friends and tortured us and killed several of my friends..."

"I was caught in the whirl pool and I knew I was going to die. No one goes over that part of the river for days at a time, but that day..."

"The Communists had killed six of my fellow missionaries and taken several others captive, we were so thankful when the American military came and took my pregnant wife and I out in a desperate evacuation effort."

"They want my scalp!"

These accounts, and many more, make this a most exciting book on missions. It contains the stories of non-traditional men and women doing a job for God under most difficult circumstances. In the end we must say, **Against all Odds...BUT GOD!**

Part I

Missionary Doctors of Chiropractic Who Used their Professional Training on the Mission Field

Operation Ethiopia

The International Chiropractors Association named Dr. Robert Thompson's work in Ethiopia, "Operation Ethiopia." Dr. Mattie Stephens of Thomaston, Georgia was its chairperson; Dr. Lyle Sherman was treasurer; and Hugh Chance of the I.C.A. legal department was legal counsel. Dr. Mattie, of course, went on to become one of the organizers and vice president of the Christian Chiropractors Association, and Dr. Lyle Sherman was the founder and namesake of Sherman College of Chiropractic in Spartanburg, South Carolina.

Dr. Robert N. Thompson

The Christian students as well as the Christians in the profession at large were very supportive of the project, and its goal of buying chiropractic equipment for Ethiopia was reached in a little over one year.

As I.C.A. officially dropped out of the project, the Christian Chiropractors Association continued with Operation Ethiopia as a means of supporting the Thompsons. C.C.A divided Operation Ethiopia into three projects:

1. The Thompson Project,
2. The Ethiopian Student Project, and
3. The Mae Hultgren Memorial Project.

Although I will deal with each of these individually, they were all part of the same effort—that of developing a permanent, self-supporting ministry in Ethiopia. Our goal was to use chiropractic as a means of bringing the gospel of Jesus Christ to Ethiopia. Although this never happened in the way in which we envisioned it in the early days of our organization, the Lord saw fit to fulfill this goal far beyond anything we could have ever dreamed.

Operation Ethiopia - Part I
The Thompson Project

When we talk about the Thompson project, remember that Mrs. Thompson was also a chiropractor; therefore, the project was rightfully the Thompsons project. We do not want to forget the many things that Dr. Hazel contributed to this ministry in Ethiopia. Even though she may not be mentioned, she was behind the scenes writing the letters, keeping the books, caring for the family (her own seven children as well as the families of the leper patients), and continuing the ministry while Dr. Bob was on his extended trips.

Even if Dr. Robert N. Thompson was not the organizer or founder of the Christian Chiropractors Association, he surely was the inspiration that brought it into being. Such an organization had been his dream for many years, and as he said, "I have a file full on the subject."

Dr. Bob's inspiring challenge stirred the 1953 Lyceum crowd to consider the opportunities for chiropractic service in foreign Christian missions. His inspiration caused some of the rest of us to unite behind a worthwhile Christian goal, and his drive and charisma brought Christians from throughout the profession together for this cause.

Robert Norman Thompson was born in Duluth, Minnesota, but his Norwegian parents moved to the prairies of southern Alberta, Canada, when he was about four years old. Bob and his two younger brothers grew up on a farm, using horses to accomplish the farm work.

At college, he earned his teaching certificate and returned to become the teacher of the one-room schoolhouse where his brothers were students. (They had to adjust to calling their brother "Mr. Thompson"!) After teaching for three years, he was challenged by an older Swedish lady to attend chiropractic college. She had helped him through teachers college and again offered to help him financially. He graduated from Palmer School of Chiropractic in Davenport, Iowa, in 1939.

While in Davenport, he met Dr. Hazel Kurth, a 1937 graduate who was one of his X-ray instructors. I'm told that Mark Rolff, a mutual friend, set them up on a blind date; however, Bob was so committed to getting an education, he did not want a woman in his life to distract him from his goal. Bob, who had never touched a drop of alcohol in his life, spent the entire evening pretending he was intoxicated in order to discourage Hazel from developing any interest in him. Obviously it did not work. He and Hazel were married on May 4, 1939, shortly after he graduated from Palmer.

Bob opened a chiropractic office in Three Hills, Alberta, where he practiced part time for about three years. Meanwhile, Canada became involved in World War II, and Bob joined the Royal Canadian Air Force. Soon he was training other pilots.

Dr. Hazel Thompson

In this capacity, he met Wing Commander Gerald Gregson, the senior chaplain at the base in Sacree, Alberta. Commander Gregson was a personal friend of Emperor Haille Selassie of Ethiopia, whom he had met while Vicar at St. Paul's church in Cambridge, England.

The Ethiopia Years

Emperor Haille Selassie had lived in exile in England since the Italians invaded his country in 1933. By 1940 the Emperor was in Khartoum, Sudan, preparing to re-enter Ethiopia. He cabled Commander Gregson to help find young men willing to assist in the liberation of Ethiopia. Gregson approached Dr. Thompson with the challenge to support the freedom fighters of Ethiopia. Gregson also persuaded the Department of Defense of Canada to reassign Thompson for duty in Ethiopia in the early months of 1943. The Allied High Command assigned Dr. Bob to Ethiopia to help Emperor Haille Selassie re-establish his government. For Dr. Bob to get out of the RCAF in the middle of the war was a miracle. At that time no one was relieved of duty for any cause. It was against all odds...BUT GOD!

Commander Gregson also introduced the Thompsons to Mr. Rowland Bingham, one of the founders of the Sudan Interior Mission (S.I.M.). Mr. Bingham advised Dr. Thompson to join the mission so that he could serve with S.I.M. after his duties with the liberation of Ethiopia were competed. The Thompsons had felt the call of the Lord to missionary service a couple of years earlier while they were attending Prairie Bible Institute in Alberta and Ethiopia was on their hearts. Ethiopia had been in the hands of the fascist government of Italy's Mussolini since 1933. The fascists were persecuting evangelical Christians, of whom there were only a few thousand before the occupation began.

By 1943 Ethiopia had been liberated. Emperor Haille Selassie was brought back to Ethiopia to re-establish his government and reconstruct his war-devastated country. The Allied High Command was in charge of this reconstruction period and needed special leaders to help the Emperor. Dr. Bob was assigned to aid in this effort. Thus the Thompsons left Canada in December 1943. Bob would later write a book on this period of history called *"Liberated: The First to Be Freed."*

Dr. Bob was responsible for establishing the Ethiopian provincial educational system. He served as its director as well as headmaster of the Haille Selassie Secondary School where most of the royal family's children were educated. He assisted in establishing the Ethiopian Air Force and trained some of its first pilots. He established the Ethiopian Boy Scouts, and as roving ambassador for the Emperor, he traveled twice to India, four times to Middle Eastern nations, and twice to Europe and North America.

In 1948 Drs. Robert and Hazel Thompson left the service of the Emperor and went into full-time missionary service with the Sudan Interior Mission (S.I.M.), an interdenominational organization serving the cause of Christ across Sub-Saharan Africa. As an S.I.M. missionary, Bob learned that the persecuted Ethiopian church had grown from a few hundred to over 20,000 during the time of the Italian occupation.

In 1952 Dr. Bob was assigned to serve with S.I.M.'s Southern Leper Colony in Sheshemane, Ethiopia, about 120 miles south of the capital, Addis Ababa. This decision was not because he was a doctor of chiropractic, but because of his leadership ability, his administrative ability, his popularity with missionaries and nationals alike, and his relationship with the Emperor. Because of his years of work with the Emperor, Bob was able to greatly assist S.I.M.'s ministry in Ethiopia.

Dr. Bob also saw this as an opportunity to use his chiropractic training in conjunction with a health ministry, not only serving traditional chiropractic patients, but also serving patients with leprosy and many other tropical diseases. Before the project got very far along; however, it was time for the Thompsons to come home for a one-year furlough.

During this furlough year, Dr. Bob was invited to speak to a gathering of 7000 to 8000 chiropractors and spouses at the 1953 Palmer School of Chiropractic Lyceum in Davenport, Iowa. During that speech Dr. Bob challenged members of the chiropractic profession to help him establish a research clinic to study chiropractic with leprosy patients. He needed chiropractic, X-ray, and laboratory equipment, which he could not afford and which the mission would not buy for him. Would these doctors join with him in this effort? Would they buy the necessary equipment and ship it to him in Ethiopia? The answer, of course, was an overwhelming "yes."

Dr. Bob knew this project was a very risky step, and that he would face much opposition. Never before had a doctor of chiropractic used chiropractic methods on a mission field. He was well aware that the service of the medical doctors and surgeons was essential to the health ministry of S.I.M. and other missions. Furthermore, he knew that in their view, chiropractic was not necessary, or at least had not been proven to be of value. If chiropractic service was to be given its rightful place in health service, he had to be careful how things were done at this stage of the program.

By 1955, Dr. Bob had his equipment and was busy taking care of patients at the Southern Leper Colony. He had 700 resident patients, mostly leper, and 800 or more non-resident patients. He was treating over 100 patients every day, giving adjustments to as many as possible and overseeing the other medical work they needed. He was also responsible for the growth and administration of the leprosarium. He had a resident medical doctor doing surgery. The work of the two doctors was mutually beneficial, and the patients received the best of both professions. The Southern Leper Colony continued to grow and was a model for all of Africa.

A Time of Opposition

The donated chiropractic equipment was a tremendous help to the mission, but, as Dr. Bob had feared, it was an irritation to some at S.I.M. headquarters in New York. They felt that what Dr. Thompson did on his own time was his business, but there should be no chiropractic service at the mission station.

Nevertheless, Dr. Bob continued to research ways to help the leprosy patients in Ethiopia. The foremost leprologist in the world, Dr. John Dreisbach was serving at the S.I.M. Kano Leprosasrium in Nigeria. He taught Dr. Bob a surgical technique for transplanting tendons from the plantar surface of the foot to the top of the foot enabling a paralyzed leper patient to walk again. The procedure was very successful. Dr. Bob incorporated this procedure into his clinic at Sheshemane and began teaching it to other doctors in East Africa who were dealing with the same problems.

Regardless of the success, the fact that a chiropractor was teaching a surgical technique to medical doctors was a disturbing report to the mission headquarters. Furthermore, by late 1955 the Southern Leper

Colony of the S.I.M. was the largest medical work in Ethiopia, and a doctor of chiropractic—not an M.D.—was in charge!

Then, in Sping 1958 a story was printed in *The Star*, a bimonthly publication of the U.S. Public Health Service Hospital in Carville, Louisiana. This was the only mainland North American hospital specifically for patients with Hansen's Disease (leprosy). Editor Stanley Stein interviewed Dr. Thompson regarding his work in Ethiopia and his use of chiropractic on leprosy patients. This centerfold story, complete with pictures, presented chiropractic in a favorable light and Dr. Thompson as a pioneer with a new approach to treating Hansen's Disease. The Christian Chiropractors Association ordered several hundred copies of *The Star* magazine and 15,000 reprints of the article featuring Dr. R. N. Thompson for distribution throughout the profession. However, because this institution was a U.S. Public Health Service hospital, the article greatly disturbed organized medicine. They put tremendous pressure on the S.I.M. board of directors to "do something about that chiropractor!"

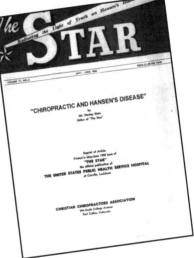

On October 17, 1958, Dr. Bob wrote:

> *"I have run into bitter medical opposition within our mission against The Star article. This is not from the medics in Ethiopia. Keep this quiet, but it is there and it is stiff. The Lord is able and I know it. This has been started by M.D.s but is being picked up by others. I've been told also that Stein (editor of The Star) is in trouble. Let us just pray and look to Him for our every portion and need."*

On November 21 he wrote:

> *"The storm has broken–all the publicity we've had, has gotten around to the S.I.M. Medical Advisory Board and they have demanded my scalp... We cannot let the S.I.M. become a battleground for the medical-chiropractic war; but it is a fight which many loyal S.I.M.ers will fight for on our side. Let us trust in the Lord and do good. We cannot stoop to low levels and keep the Lord on our side. Prov. 3:5,6 is true!"*

On November 29 he wrote:

"The S.I.M. West African Field Medical Advisory Committee have demanded my scalp. There are many implications and complications and it threatens an upheaval in the S.I.M. We cannot make a mission a professional battleground. We must show a Christian spirit and attitude in each step–even if they don't. Therefore if the charges are not withdrawn, I will resign. My tentative resignation is already in. These medical committee members, who really have nothing to do with me or my work, have demanded:

1. I "divorce" myself from the practice of chiropractic;

2. I "renounce" the title of doctor; and

3. I sever all chiropractic association connections.

"They also say I am not fit for leadership in the S.I.M., as it would reflect on the 'integrity and intelligence' of the S.I.M. They also condemn chiropractic as a 'false cult theory and a menace to public health.' There are many friends on the inside who will fight–even some of our council. But our general director, Dr. A. D. Helzer, tends to agree with them and is afraid to fight. They need their M.D.s and don't have to have us. None of these M.D.s know me personally, we have just met."

On December 22, 1958, Dr. Bob wrote the following:

"I have just heard from the East Africa Field Council–a copy of their letter to Dr. A. D. Helzer (S.I.M. general director)–signed by the field council of nine men plus the field director and the field secretary. One of these men is an M.D. They confirm their complete confidence in the character, integrity, ability and service of the two Drs. Thompson and will welcome them back to the field in any capacity any time. They also rebuked the West Africa Field Medical Committee. I do not know the end result, but we still feel we are through with the S.I.M.–more can be gained for the Lord and for chiropractic by our not yielding one inch. Pray with us yet please."

It needs to be understood that at that time mission societies were very dependent on medical personnel, doctors as well as nurses who were in short supply, to carry on their medical outreach. Incorporating a health ministry into a mission outreach was a most effective adjunct to evangelism. Also at that time, organized medicine had a strangle hold on mission societies; they dictated whether or not a doctor could serve with the society and whether the society had its "medical accreditation." No mission society would dare come into disfavor with the powers of organized medicine if they were to have any hope of continuing a medical outreach.

Dr. Bob had now made at least three fatal blunders in the eyes of organized medicine (heading up a medical work, teaching surgery to M.D.s, and being featured in *The Star*), and they put the pressure on the S.I.M. board of directors in New York. Even though the S.I.M. missionaries (including the medical doctors) on the East African field fully supported Dr. Bob and his work, and even though his fellow missionaries had elected him S.I.M. field director for all of East Africa, the West African Medical Committee and the North American medical powers wanted this chiropractor out of the Southern Leper Colony. In an effort to pacify the medical community, the executive director of the Sudan Interior Mission, A. D. Helzer, Ph.D. suggested reassigning the Thompsons to Australia. Dr. Bob responded, "God has not appointed me to Australia!" He knew his ministry in Ethiopia was over. Thus ended the mission career of one of the greatest missionary statesmen of the twentieth century.

Emperor Haille Selassie was so concerned about the Thompsons leaving Ethiopia that he did not summon Bob but drove 120 miles from his palace in Addis Ababa over horrible roads to personally say good-by to this, his most trusted friend. For the work that Dr. Robert N. Thompson did for Ethiopia and its ruler, Emperor Haille Selassie, Dr. Thompson was given the Star of Ethiopia Award. This is the highest civilian award given by the Emperor, and Dr. Bob is the only non-Ethiopian to ever receive it.

Officially it was recorded that the Thompsons resigned from S.I.M. due to the health of their children. The Thompsons had three daughters and four sons. Three of the four boys, George, David, and Makonnen had a form of mental retardation which at that time was not understood. (Many years later they learned that these three boys and a fourth one, Stephen born in 1959, had a genetic disease known as Fragile X Chromosome Disease. This disease is carried by the mother and passed on to her sons. All but their son Paul had the condition.) It is true that the Thompsons had considered leaving the field for their sakes. However, the issue that forced the decision went much deeper than that.

Dr. Thompson was caught in the crossfire of the war between organized medicine and the chiropractic profession. This war, which had been going on for many years and continued on for several years to come, spilled over from its professional base into the church and the mission societies. Dr. Otis S. Warr, specialist in internal medicine, Fellow with the American College of Physicians, and active staff member at Baptist Hospital in Memphis, made the following comments before the ministerial association of Memphis, Tennessee:

> *"The time spent in preparation and the curriculum studied by chiropractors is an insult to our civilization and to God. The medical profession needs the support of church leaders in eradicating this and similar cults from our society! ... (Chiropractors) join churches to get the prestige and an air of respectability the Church can give them."*

Dr. Warr's speech was published in the Cumberland Presbyterian in January 1959. This, and many similar attacks, was spawned by the publicity which Dr. Thompson had received in Christian circles because of the work he had been doing in Ethiopia and of course by the publicity it received in *The Star.*

Organized medicine was using the church and its mission societies to carry out their ostracism and character assassination of chiropractic and chiropractors. It is sad to say, but the church and its mission societies were powerless to fight this commanding political force. It was against all odds...BUT GOD!

We knew Satan was attempting to prevent the success of Dr. Thompson as well as the fledgling Christian Chiropractors Association; however, we also new we must press on with God's plan for this movement. Quoting from the March 1959 issue of the *Christian Chiropractor*, "The best way to tell if you are really working for Christ is when the Devil throws all Hell at you. Let's be willing to suffer a little persecution for the sake of what we know is right."

The Political Years

A very dear friend of the Thompsons, Premier E.C. Manning was not only Premier of the Province of Alberta, Canada, and national leader of the Social Credit Party of Canada but also an outstanding Christian with a nationwide Bible study program on the radio every week.

Dr. Bob was convinced that Manning should run for Prime Minister of Canada. During the last half of 1958 and 1959, Bob spoke to his Christian audiences in Canada on behalf of Premier Manning. However, when it came time for the next election, Premier Manning backed out and nominated Dr. Robert N. Thompson to be national leader of the Social Credit Party and candidate for Prime Minister.

In the 1961election, Bob Thompson was elected to the Canadian Parliament, and as neither of the two major parties held a majority, they needed Bob Thompson and his Social Credit Party to form the new government. Bob held the balance of power; he had tremendous political influence in all of Canada's national affairs.

During this time, as well as after Dr. Bob's service in the Canadian Parliament, he mediated several international crises, including the Biafran War in Nigeria and the revolt in Congo. He was in the forefront of opening up China to the West and finding a solution to the Vietnamese war.

Bob went on to serve eight years in the Canadian Parliament, six years as president of the Canadian Memorial Chiropractic College, and professor and vice president of Trinity Western University in British Columbia. He earned his Ph.D. in political science at the age of 75. He also was sent on many diplomatic missions all over the world by the Canadian government and the United Nations. He was Canadian delegate to the United Nations and also to the North American Treaty Organization. He served on the boards of many organizations including Samaritan's Purse (the relief and development arm of the Billy Graham Evangelistic Association which is headed by Rev. Franklin Graham), Gospel Recordings, World Vision, and Mission Aviation Fellowship. He was a life member of Gideons, Int. and also of the Canadian Boy Scouts.

In 1985, Dr. Thompson received Canada's highest civilian medal of honor, the Lifestyle Citizenship Award, presented to him by the Prime Minister on behalf of all Canadians. In 1991 he was awarded the Officer of the Order of Canada. One of his last duties was that of commissioner on the National Parole Board of Canada.

The Later Years

In February 1986 Dr. Bob had a severe heart attack which predicated a 5 by-pass operation under emergency conditions. By June, however, he was well enough to attend the annual C.C.A. convention in the Black Hills of South Dakota. In August he was one of the hosts to 10,000 Christian leaders from all over the world at the Billy Graham Association's "Amsterdam 86" conference in Amsterdam, The Netherlands.

Dr. Bob never lost touch with the Christian Chiropractors Association and could always be called upon for counsel and advice. He and Hazel appeared at many C.C.A. meetings around the United States and Canada. Dr. Bob often talked about some early life lessons which guided him in later years.

He told of plowing a field with a horse as a young man. He learned to keep his eyes focused on a landmark at the far end of the field in order to plow a straight row. Looking at the furrow at his feet, looking the furrow next to him, or looking behind him would cause him to plow a crooked furrow or lose track of where he was going. So it is in life, he said. If we lose track of our goal, compare ourselves with others around us, or look at where we have been, we will not get to where we want to go.

Dr. Bob also told of a lesson he learned while flying an airplane. He noticed that rivers and creeks always find the path of least resistance as they amble across the countryside and are gobbled up by ever-larger bodies of water. Men are the same way if they follow the path of least resistance. "The path of least resistance," he said, "is the way you get crooked rivers and crooked men!" Strong men will fight against the easy way, will keep their eyes on the goal, and will have the conviction, will power, and determination to set lofty goals and to attain them.

In a speech to the South Carolina Chiropractic Association, Dr. Bob shared that he had three convictions in life:

1. *"I believe there is a God. I believe it with all of my heart. If there wasn't any God, there would be no hope."*

2. *"My second conviction, which is basic to my way of life, is that I believe that God has a plan for me in my daily life."* And

3. *"I believe in chiropractic. I believe that chiropractic is a gift from God. I believe that it was given to us in our generation to be used, not to get us rich, not to give us a good living, not to make us respected in our community as professional people. No, It was given to us to help us to help those who are sick. God planned it so."*

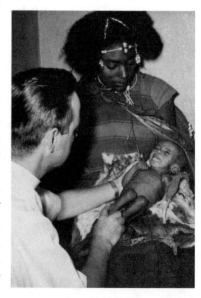

By these principles Dr. Robert N. Thompson lived his life as a humble teacher in a one-room country school, as an officer in the Royal Canadian Air Force, as a confidant and emissary for the Emperor of Ethiopia, as a member of Canadian Parliament, as an emissary for the United Nations, and as a missionary chiropractor. The same hand that shook the hands of

presidents and prime ministers also gave aid, comfort–and chiropractic adjustments–to the leper, the poor, and the most severely disad-
vantaged in one of the world's poorest nations.

Dr. Bob lost his beloved wife, helpmeet, and companion on
July 14, 1992. Dr. Hazel had been the healthier of the two in their
later lives. And although she suffered, she succumbed rather quickly
to cancer of the liver.

Dr. Bob later married Evelyn Brandt, the widow of a fellow missionary to Ethiopia, whom he had known and worked with for many
years. Evelyn was a great help and support in his final years.

Dr. Bob died on November 16, 1997. His funeral was held in the
Trinity Western University auditorium and was attended by thousands
of friends and dignitaries. Rev. Franklin Graham delivered the message. The lessons we learned from Dr. Bob we will never forget.

Operation Ethiopia - Part II
The Ethiopian Student Project

When Dr. Robert N. Thompson took over the Southern Leper Colony of the Sudan Interior Mission (S.I.M.) at Sheshemane, Ethiopia, in 1954, he knew that he ultimately needed to work himself out of a job. From the be-

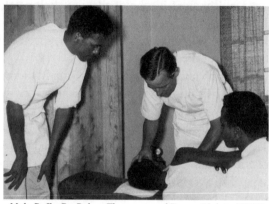

Mulu Baffa, Dr. Robert Thompson and Beyene Mulattu (1956)

ginning he began to train Ethiopians to care for the sick, including lepers. S.I.M. had provided an excellent team of workers for the mission station, including a medical doctor, nurses, evangelists, and an agriculturist. But each missionary was asked to train Ethiopians to eventually take over.

Within three years the station had trained Ethiopian nurses, aids, and agriculturists. Dr. Bob was especially impressed with three young men who showed exceptional promise as nurse practitioners. He had even taught them some rudimentary chiropractic adjusting procedures. It was Dr. Bob's dream that these three men study chiropractic in the United States and return to Ethiopia to carry on the work that he had started.

This had never been done! There were so many obstacles. Could the young men learn English well enough to compete on the college level? Could these three, from a third world tribal village adjust to the social and cultural challenges of America? Would a chiropractic college accept Africans at a time when most colleges and universities did not accept students of "color?" And finally, how could any effort of this size be paid for? It was against all odds...BUT GOD!

Beyene Mulattu at Leprosarium (1956)

Getting the Students to Chiropractic College

Dr. Bob contacted the Christian Chiropractors Association, which at that time was a fledging organization of barely 100 members. He then contacted Palmer School of Chiropractic in Davenport, Iowa, where many of us received our chiropractic education and where he had given his speech in 1953 informing the profession about his work in Ethiopia. The school agreed to accept the Ethiopian men in spite of their stand against "colored." They were concerned whether the men could handle the language and whether their scholastic ability was adequate. We agreed to do the testing after they arrived, and Dr. B.J. Palmer personally agreed to waive the tuition costs and provide special counsel for them.

The C.C.A. notified the members about the opportunity to sponsor the Ethiopian students for four years at Palmer School of Chiropractic. Support came in almost immediately from members and non-members alike, and in only a few months we had enough pledges that we felt it was safe to cable Dr. Thompson to prepare to send at least two of the young men. We would see that they got an education and send them back to Ethiopia. In the meantime, Dr. Thompson had persuaded Ethiopia's Emperor Haile Selassie to pay the transportation costs to send the men to America. With the transportation costs covered, the tuition waived, and the pledges in hand–all doors appeared to be open.

About that time, Dr. Thompson received orders from S.I.M. to return to the States, which he did August 1, 1957, with Dr. Hazel and their children. Mulu Baffa and Beyenne Mulattu came to the U.S. and started Palmer College in Davenport, Iowa, on October 1. Dr. Bob spent two and a half months in the U.S. and Canada before placing Hazel and the family in Red Deer, Alberta, and returning to Ethiopia alone on November 1 to reports

Mulu Baffa and Beyene Mulattu at Palmer School

of serious problems. He wrote the following letter to me on Nov. 19, 1957.

> "My two and a half months at home was a real mountain top experience of blessing. This was true in North America and also in Britain and France. As I look back on the renewed friendship with many and the new friendships established with others, and at the wonderful courtesy and fellowship with all we came in contact with, causes me to realize again the ever faithfulness of our God. Again I can just say 'Praise His Blessed Name.'

> "However, when you have mountains you must of necessity have valleys, and I realized that fact very vividly as I returned and was pushed down deep into a valley of medical and anti-Christian opposition. This had built up while I was away, partly because there had been too much publicity in our favor on one hand, and towards the going of Mulu and Beyenne to study chiropractic on the other.

> "There was an attempt to stop the boys from going and when that failed, an attempt was made to divert them to 'other' studies. The money promised for their travel was also sidetracked and has not yet been paid. Fortunately my mission administration officers were loyal and advanced the money on loan so they could leave on schedule. As yet this money has not been received and my own feeling is that we do not want it when it has been 'dirtied' as it has. God's work does not require the world's money, and I am sure that He will in His faithfulness justify this stand in meeting this unexpected expenditure which I am responsible for.

> "The Medical Board (which is controlled by Western medical doctors and advisors) has even been responsible for charging the mission of not properly staffing the leprosarium with qualified doctors. However, insofar as it is possible as a Christian missionary, I have answered the unjust charges and trust God for the rest. The people continue to come in great numbers, even government officials and foreign people who are ill. Always I remember that God is faithful, and He will care for and justify His own. Chiropractic has been discussed over and over by these foreign M.D.s in their meetings and also with myself."

Over $1600 transportation money had been confiscated by the Ethiopian Medical Board (controlled by North American and European medical interests). In 1957, $1600 was a very large sum of money for either Bob Thompson or the C.C.A. to repay to S.I.M. However,

God was still working. When the
Emperor himself found out what
had happened, he personally saw
that the money was released and
the debt was paid. He also sent the
Ethiopian chairman of the Ethiopian Medical Board out of the
country. (He could do nothing
about the foreign advisors.)

Had Mulu Baffa and Beyenne
Mulattu been prevented from coming to the U.S., the entire history
of the C.C.A. might have been

Mulu Baffa (1956)

changed. Furthermore, had medical opposition, which presumably
originated in the U.S., been successful, we would have had no Ethiopian Student Project. Ethiopia would have been deprived of the leadership that Dr. Mulatu Baffa later gave to the church and his nation.
Of course, this opposition was not silenced when this effort was
thwarted; it was only the first of many attempts to destroy the ministry of the Thompsons and keep chiropractic out of Ethiopia. Later
that same year, Dr. Thompson's work was turned over to medical missionary doctors. When Drs. Baffa and Mulattu returned from their
chiropractic training, they too would feel the sting of this opposition.

Dr. Mulu Baffa and Dr. Beyene Mulattu graduated from Palmer School
of Chiropractic on September 24, 1960, with Dr. Robert N. Thompson as
their graduation speaker. After graduation they accompanied Dr. Thompson to Alberta, Canada, for the chiropractic licensing board exams.
The Alberta license, together with the Doctor of Chiropractic degree from
Palmer gave them the legal right to practice chiropractic.

Hundreds of people had contributed to the success of this project.
Doctors and laymen had donated money and equipment. Mr. Norman
Ross gave them an apartment at reduced rent in Davenport, Iowa.
Grandview Baptist Church generously received the men into their fellowship and helped them in many ways. Dr. Ernest Napolitano of
Columbia Institute of Chiropractic donated return travel expenses and
equipment. Dr. B. J. Palmer donated the tuition scholarships, and Mr.
Bill Nordquist, photographer, even took pictures of the young men
around the college and donated the photos for use in promotion and
public relations. Mulu and Beyenne were well received by fellow
students, and some of them have been life long friends.

After their graduation, Dr. Herbert C. Hender, Dean of Palmer School of Chiropractic wrote this letter:

> *"Let it be known that Drs. Mulu Baffa and Beyenne Mulattu joined with us here at the PSC to make their schooling a complete success. They were liked by most everyone, and were regarded by their classmates and the faculty as very valuable members of the student body. You will gather that we here at the PSC feel that the Baffa-Mulattu project was a complete success.*
>
> *"Thank you for expressing the appreciation of the C.C.A. but I could say that the project was a 'two-way street' in which we both did our part, and believe we were duly rewarded. We now wish these two fine young chiropractors the best of everything in their future activities."*
>
> *Cordially,*
> *Herbert C. Hender, Dean, Palmer School of Chiropractic*

The Ethiopian Chiropractors Return Home

Upon returning to Ethiopia in November 1960, Dr. Mulu Baffa applied for a license to practice chiropractic. The application had to be filed with the Board of Health, with its Ethiopian minister, and with its foreign medical advisors–the very people who had tried to stop him from going to the U.S.A. in 1957. These same advisors had accused Dr. Robert Thompson of not being qualified to run the Southern Leper Colony in 1958. (The Ethiopian Minister on the Board had been replaced but not the foreign board members.) On July 6th 1961, Dr. Baffa wrote the following:

Mulattu and Alemai Baffa wedding photo (1956)

> *"I do not know where to start to tell you the report of ourselves but permit me to inform you briefly starting from the time of my return.*
>
> *"Arriving in Ethiopia safely in November by the good care of our Shepherd and Lord, I presented my documents to the Ministry of Public Health with an application for permission and recognition to practice chiropractic. I saw some government*

officials with whom I had a previous contact. Then due to the delay of the matter of permissions, we went down to the south of the country to see the project and to visit family for about six weeks.

"Then I returned to Addis Ababa to check how far the things have progressed. The documents went through the board of medical men. The board made a recommendation that we should attend a short course in Public Health College and the recommendation was approved by the minister who seems helpful but afraid to differ with the board. After having several long discussions about chiropractic and its philosophy with the minister, he asked me to work in one of our large hospitals of the city at least for a few months in order to see what chiropractic is and does. I accepted this offer temporarily and am working in this hospital now.

"To start with, there were just a handful of patients at the department. Within a few weeks time the number of patients daily was tripled and today the daily number of patients averages from 45 to 50. The results are just marvelous yet it is unfortunate that the major opposers of chiropractic are the foreigners on the board. The jealousy still exists regardless of the results. Due to the fact that I have a few patients that I care for outside the hospital, a complaint came up against me a few days ago from the Ministry of Public Health. In the hospital at the Physiotherapy Department I can check the patient and adjust him accordingly, (but not on the outside.)

"With the head doctors of the hospital, we made several discussions on chiropractic. It seems many of them cannot grasp it, yet, there are several who fully recognize chiropractic. I have been able to establish good contacts and friendship among many doctors who are in Addis.

"Before and after Beyenne came, we made several trips to the Ministry regarding the permission. The board is to have another meeting sometime in July to reconsider the matter. So please join us in prayer so that God may direct their minds to make an unselfish decision for His glory and honor."

Legal permission to practice chiropractic was never granted because of the North American and European members on the medical board. The Ethiopian health minister and the other Ethiopian officials never had a problem with granting the license but could not overrule the decisions of the foreigners.

The fact that they did not get licenses to practice chiropractic did not prevent them from having a health ministry, or using chiropractic in conjunction with their other responsibilities. Dr. Beyenne Mulattu became hospital administrator at the Mennonite Mission Hospital in Nazareth, Ethiopia, and stayed there for many years until he retired. During his tenure at the hospital, he continued to use his chiropractic training at every opportunity.

Dr. Mulattu Baffa became administrator of the segregation village of the Southern Leper Colony at Sheshemane for the S.I.M. and started with 500 leper patients; that soon expanded to close to 30,000. In February 1969 Dr. Baffa wrote the following:

"In the months of January and February, I have been very busy traveling to the surrounding sub-districts to establish more clinics and examining the villagers. In these two months some 22,000 cases have been examined and 150 new cases registered.

"There is a tremendous opportunity for the Gospel witness. I take along a crew of bandage dressers, and an evangelist in a Land Rover. Sometimes there are some areas, which are highly mountainous, to which we take mules and horses. We pitch our tents in a given village and start examining the villagers until we are through with every one in that village and then move on to the next. We are hoping to have a mobile clinic in the near future."

The Communists Take Over

In 1974 a Communist uprising swept the country of Ethiopia. The Emperor was murdered and a Russian- and Cuban-dominated government was put in place. Dr. Baffa was beaten and put in jail. Several of his friends were executed. When they came for him, a young Communist soldier, whom Mulu had befriended when he was but a child, stood up for him and would not let the soldiers execute him:

"As you may know, several political and economical changes have taken place in our country which have affected various areas of our work and our personal life. Most of what we had invested was nationalized, including the rural and urban properties. A month ago, some local people at Sheshemane marched up against several leading Christian brothers including myself, enforcing me to go through a physical torture which I hesitate to mention in this letter. The entire work at Sheshemane is greatly hampered, and many unfavorable voices are rising up against the church.

"God has spared my life in a wonderful way, and for the time being, my whole family has been able to move up to Addis Ababa. However, we were not able to move out any of our personal possessions from Sheshemane. We praise His Name for the safety of the family. Although we have very little to live on, we trust that our 'God is able to supply all our needs accord-

ing to His riches.' With Paul, I can say: 'I know both how to be abased and I know how to abound; everywhere and in all things I am instructed both to be full and to be hungry, both to abound and to suffer need.' 'I can do all things through Christ which strengthens me.'"

Dr. Baffa went on to become the executive director of the Kale Heywet church, the national indigenous church of Ethiopia. When the Communists seized the country in 1974, Kale Heywet had almost 3000 churches; but under intense persecution, that number grew tremendously. By the time of the overthrow of the Communists in 1991, the church, under the leadership of Dr. Baffa, had grown to almost 4000 congregations!

When I visited Ethiopia in 2001, Kale Heywet had 4500 churches with over 4,000,000 members; 200 Bible schools, 3 seminaries including over 3000 students in theological extension studies; and 150,000 young people involved in their youth ministries. The Church also has 222 home missionaries and evangelists and 16 foreign missionaries in India and Pakistan. Furthermore, Kale Heywet has developed pure water projects–drilling wells, putting up windmills and developing surface springs–serving 250,000 people in remote villages. They have 14 medical clinics staffed with nurses and physicians, and a medical director at the headquarters. Headquarters is a new four-story administration building in the heart of Addis Ababa. All of this, and much more, came under the leadership of Dr. Mulattu Baffa.

During the Communist days, Dr. Baffa was jailed and persecuted unmercifully, but through it all he gained a reputation with the government as one who could be trusted, one who would not relinquish his beliefs. Because of his upstanding character, the government appointed him to head up the famine relief and agricultural development in northern Ethiopia and allowed him to travel extensively to Europe and North America soliciting aid for the victims of famine. (This he did in addition to his ministry with Kale Heywet.)

To aid in the Ethiopian famine relief, the Christian Chiropractors Association started a garden seed program. In 1982, 6600 pounds of garden seed were sent, and Dr. Mulu Baffa and his workers distributed it to farmers all over the country. In this way we were able to help the Ethiopian people help themselves solve the famine problem by helping them produce their own home grown food. Each year the C.C.A. sent garden seed to Ethiopia, and in 1984, 13,000 pounds of seed were shipped.

Operation Ethiopia - Part III
Mae Hultgren Memorial Project

The third phase of the Operation Ethiopia Project, which the Christian Chiropractors Association undertook, was first called the Ethiopian School Project. Dr. Robert N. Thompson had a vision for a chiropractic school in conjunction with a training center for other health sciences and nursing. It was to be a place where Ethiopians could be trained to do village medicine, dentistry, nursing, and simple chiropractic procedures. This was soon changed to emphasize more of a clinic and mission outreach center which would be self supporting and which would also be able to teach and train Ethiopians to evangelize as well as learn health and hygiene concepts to serve in the villages in the area.

Emperor Haille Selassie's daughter gave Dr. Thompson two hundred acres of land near the Ethiopian town of Wando, along with a loan of approximately $4,000 to develop the project. Wando is 150 miles south of the Ethiopian capital Addis Ababa and about 30 miles south of Sheshemane where Dr. Thompson headed a leprosarium. The land was in a semi tropical valley with lush vegetation, hot springs, and a summer home occupied by the Princess. Dr. Thompson deeded it to Mulu Baffa, Beyenne Mulattu, and Yohannes Makeeso, three young men who had been working with Dr. Thompson at the Sheshemane Leprosarium.

Dr. Thompson hoped that planting coffee trees on the property would produce enough income in three to four years to develop the project and to eventually make it a self-supporting mission outreach station. As coffee is a big cash crop in Ethiopia and Ethiopian coffee is in great demand in Europe, this seemed to be a wise decision. Yohannes Makeeso was put in charge of the project while Mulu Baffa and Beyenne Mulattu were studying chiropractic in the U.S.

On September 19, 1957, as this project was in the planning stage, my mother, Mae A. Hultgren, died. When a number of memorial gifts came in, my family decided to

Mae A. Hultgren
1906 -1959

use that money as a permanent memorial to her by sending it Ethiopia to buy coffee trees and help in the development of this third phase of Operation Ethiopia. The members of the C.C.A. joined in, as did other members of the chiropractic profession, and over the next few years several thousand dollars was sent to Ethiopia.

The following letter, received in November 1959 from Mr. H. W. Waldock of the Sudan Interior Mission at the Sheshemane leprosarium, tells of the early struggles of the project and of the evangelistic opportunities that the opened in the valley.

"Mr. Yohannes Makeeso has asked me if I would write to you expressing his personal thanks, as well as those of us who are vitally connected with the Wando Project, for the gifts which you have sent out to us to date. We have received the checks and we are indeed grateful to you for your interest in us and in our work.

"No doubt Dr. Thompson has told you much about Wando Valley. It is indeed a beautiful spot and we wish you could have the privilege of seeing it yourselves. The project is coming along very nicely and the man in charge of the work program has done an excellent job. We have been finding it rather a burden financially, as the project will not really begin to be self-supporting for about another year. However, the money, which we are receiving from you, is a big help in helping us to develop this project.

"I know you will be interested in the work of the Lord in the valley. We have recently rejoiced over a good number that have come to know the Lord. Our two national evangelists have been willing to undergo hardship and difficulty for the sake of the Gospel, and the Lord seems to have blessed them in the salvation of a number. Because of their boldness and faithfulness in witnessing, almost an entire village of around 40 turned to the Lord, and yesterday as I inquired concerning these people, I was happy to hear that they were zealous for the Lord. Then too, there have been others in other places that have turned to the Lord. They are sponsoring a small school and this is another cause for rejoicing, for many of the children are being taught to read and are given basic elementary training which will increase their effectiveness as witnesses for the Lord.

"I must close. We do thank you for what you are doing for us and we do appreciate this link to the Christian Chiropractors Association. We ask that you extend our sincere thanks to them for their gifts and for their interest in us as we seek to do His will."

Another letter received in December 1961 from Mr. Bruce Bond of the S.I.M. details some further development of this project:

"On behalf of Wando Emmaus, I am writing this letter. Perhaps I should introduce myself first of all. For many years now I have been working at the leprosarium where Dr. Thompson was associated. It was during this time that the idea of Wando Emmaus came into being, and during the absence of Mulu and Beyene I have been in charge of keeping the place going. Now with Beyene's return, much of the responsibility has been taken from me, and now I act purely as an advisor to the project. My training is as an agriculturalist and horticulturalist and so Wando has been a paradise in this field of science.

"You no doubt wonder how we use your money which is so greatly appreciated. Actually the project started with nothing but a piece of land, 200 acres in extent, which was covered in brush. First, of all this had to be cleared, stumped, and planted. At present we have nearly 40,000 coffee trees and for the upkeep of this project alone, we require a large income. Perhaps this year, our income will keep up with our expenses but our great aim is to be a self-supporting Christian project, which will be to the Glory of His Name.

"As yet buildings have not yet been commenced apart from one very small two room building where Beyene and his wife are living. Our goal of course, is for a large school, a clinic, and adequate living quarters for Beyene, Mulu and Yohannes, who is the third member of our team.

"Perhaps you would be interested to know that Mulu has joined the staff of the Sheshemane leprosarium and will be administrator of a nearby large segregation village with 500 patients attached. Both men have a wonderful testimony for the Lord, and both would have me send their special New Year greeting to all of you who have so wonderfully helped us."
Bruce H. Bond, S.I.M.

On May 10, 1962, Dr. Mulu Baffa sent the following letter tying together several of the events that were transpiring in Ethiopia.

"Greetings in the sweetest Name of our Lord. Time of many months have passed since I got back to Ethiopia. Though in my part I failed to correspond with you very much. I have no doubt that we are still being remembered on your prayer list. God had led and guided us wonderfully.

"Permit me to inform you briefly with our past year's experience   Finally when Beyene got back, it was my intention to see His Majesty, the Emperor, but due to various reasons

such as a small revolution last year, and the death of the Empress and also of the Prince, who died a few weeks ago, we were not able to see him personally.

"Beyenne, upon his return, started working in Wando Emmaus. He got married and now they have a month old baby boy.

"Then in Addis Ababa, the S.I.M. asked me to take over the responsibility of a newly opened leprosarium. We prayed about the matter for some months and several others joined with us in prayer. So we felt the definite guiding of the Lord to take this opportunity. So we came down to Sheshemane four months ago.

"At the moment I am doing more or less a developmental work at the new project. For the time being, staying where Bob T. used to live at the Southern Leper Colony at Sheshemane, and I am also doing a chiropractic work in the clinic. I have my table in there and have access to use the X-ray.

"A British female medical doctor is very cooperative. Now I have in hand a patient who came from Addis suffering the pain of an intervertebral disc herniation. Being in hospitals for many months and having no hope, inquired for some other remedy. A friend of his told him about chiropractic and our address. He came down some weeks ago and now he is ready to go back to his work. How gratifying it is to see people helped physically and spiritually. I am also doing some traveling in Ethiopia for spiritual conferences.

"The chiropractic project at Wando Emmaus is developing very nicely. Coffee and fruit trees are just excellent. Beyenne is now with the Mennonite Mission near Addis. Bruce Bond, missionary agriculturalist from Sheshemane, is very helpful in the plantation. Both him and I, being very close to the project, we often go down to it together. Thanks for another check yesterday morning. I wouldn't know what we would have done without the C.C.A. aid.

"God has blessed us physically and spiritually and it is still our hope to have a legal right to practice. Pray for us and our greetings to all our good friends."
In Christ, Mulu, Alemai, Mizan and Akililu

Another letter received from Bruce Bond of the S.I.M. in August of 1962 further updates the progress of the Wando Emmaus Project.

"First of all, may I send you our special Christian greetings. At this time we would like to express to you our gratitude for your continual help throughout the past three years.

"Secondly, I am sure that you are all anxious to know how the development of the project at Wando is progressing. This

present week, we are making a start on our elementary school, which we trust will open in the new year. You will understand that these many children surrounding this area have never before in their lives had the opportunity of going to school. We have now cleared the forest and planted over fifty-five thousand coffee trees. This in itself is a very large project but now gradually we are starting to show signs of a profit from the plantation. Once the project is satisfactorily established, we will use the profits to carry on the development of the project.

"Thirdly, may we take this opportunity to relate to you some of our problems? Dr. Mulu over the past year has made continual representation to the Ministry of Health for permission to establish a clinic but so far, all permission has been denied. Will you please pray with us that this situation will shortly be changed so that Christ's name might be glorified down at Wando.

"Fourthly, just a brief word about the two men you helped to train over the past few years. Dr. Beyenne has now taken the responsibility of Administrator of the Mennonite Mission Hospital. Dr. Mulu is administrator of the new segregation village for five hundred lepers. Both men have very responsible positions and God is blessing them in their witness.
Sincerely in Him, Bruce H. Bond"

A follow up letter received from Mr. Bond in November 1963 told of progress, but frustration at the slow movement at times.

"Your very generous help over the years has certainly enabled us to establish the project at Wando Valley. As I previously stated, your help was needed until April and from then we have carefully budgeted our expenses to enable us to carry on throughout the year. As I see the situation at Wando, it will be a struggle for the next six months and after that we should really be on the winning side.

"As far as the establishment of chiropractic ministry, I am afraid nothing has been done or will likely be done for the present. In the future when certain things change in the country, I am sure we will see the clinic established. Actually, Beyenne and Mulu are both very interested in living down at Wando; and when the day arrives that the project can support them, they will be the first ones to take the opportunity. Things move very slowly in these countries but eventually we see changes taking place.
Yours Sincerely, Bruce"

Therefore, due to pressure from the foreign medical personal on the Ethiopian Health Ministry, no direct chiropractic mission outreach was ever established in the Wando valley. I visited the Wando project in 1968 and saw the coffee harvest. It was a thrill to see coffee beans drying in the sun and observe the entire process of preparing them for market. A community school had been built as well as several other buildings for the project, but it had no health ministry outreach. However, a local evangelist was working successfully in the area, and Jesus Christ was being glorified.

In 1974 when a Marxist revolution took over Ethiopia, the government confiscated the Wando property and turned it into a resort for government officials. By Ethiopian standards it became a fantastic resort/spa complete with restaurant, cabins, gift shop and hot spring swimming pools. All of the coffee trees were torn out, and replaced with sugar cane and bananas. It was still that way when I visited in 2001.

The chiropractic ministry was never fully developed as we envisioned, yet in spite of the efforts of organized medicine and the foreign control of the Ethiopian Health Ministry it was never crushed. Dr. Beyenne Mulattu's ministry with the Mennonite Hospital and Dr. Mulattu Baffa's leadership with the Kale Heywat church have perhaps done more than our plans to aid the advance of Christianity in that part of the world. The spiritual ministry of the entire Operation Ethiopia Project will be fully known only in eternity.

Bolivia
Dr. and Mrs. J. Bridgens Johnson

As Dr. and Mrs. J. Bridgens Johnson were driving across the country in early summer1958, they made a point to visit my office in Bismarck, North Dakota, to check out the Christian Chiropractors Association. Dr. and Mrs. Johnson were missionaries for the Church of the Open Door of Philadelphia in the country of Bolivia.

The First Chiropractic Adjustments in South America

Dr. Johnson, from Philadelphia, graduated from a small Pennsylvania college of chiropractic in 1937 and did some post-graduate work with the Lincoln College of Chiropractic in 1943. He practiced for a short time in Pennsylvania before leaving for the jungles of Peru in 1938. He had only a home made wooden portable adjusting table, which the termites found very delectable and soon destroyed.

Even though he was sent to Peru not as a chiropractor but as a church planting missionary, he found many opportunities to use his professional training. Creatively stretching a patient across an overturned canoe, a shipping trunk, or a large fallen tree, he would do his best to deliver a chiropractic adjustment. Here's Dr. Johnson's own description of his first adjustment on a Peruvian Indian:

Dr. J. Bridgens Johnson

"At various times I had given adjustments to my missionary friend and his family for headaches. One day, while in the midst of getting things ready to move, there appeared at the door a group of Indians who had come down to help. They had been traveling down the headwaters of the Amazon all day in their canoe in the hot sun and consequently all had quite severe headaches.

"So it was that my fellow missionary suggested that they submit themselves for an adjustment, not only for the sake of the relief that they would get from the adjustment but also to see their reaction to this type of treatment. I gave a few simple cervical adjustments. Soon they were all talking about the quick relief they got as well as

laughing at the surprise each one got as they heard the snap of the vertebrae being adjusted.

"After these new Indian patients transported him down the river to the tribe where he was to be working, they quickly began to spread the word.

"The Indians whom I had adjusted got busy telling everybody else how they had gotten rid of their headaches. One of the most interested listeners to their story was an old Indian witch doctor or medicine man. He asked me to wait for him while he started up the road and soon came back with... a roundup of the sick in the village... [An interpreter related the] complaints of each one, then he asked me to take over.] I spotted a canoe close by which was in the process of being hollowed out from a large tree...This turned out to be the first adjusting table ever used by a chiropractor in South America."

Later Dr. Johnson shared the following:

"I found chiropractic readily accepted in the small jungle Indian tribe where I worked. They had been accustomed to keeping their spines in shape by walking up and down on each other's backs. They lie face down on the ground and the one who is treating shifts his weight from heel to heel as he stands on the back of his companion with his heels resting over the transverse processes of the vertebrae."

An Unusual Missionary Couple

About the same time that Dr. Bridge, as he was called, had gone to Peru, Dorothy Mohr, a missionary from the same church in Philadelphia, had gone to Bolivia. They both returned on furlough in 1943. During that furlough their relationship grew, and they were married in Philadelphia.

Dorothy Johnson

This was not the typical missionary couple, however. At eighteen months old, Dorothy had contracted polio and the lower half of her body was totally paralyzed. In 1939 this single woman, legs in braces, hobbling on crutches, with all the courage she could muster, went alone to a people she learned to love, the Indians of Bolivia.

After a short period of time in the U.S. for additional studies, they returned to the lowland jungles of northeastern Bolivia in 1946 to work among a leper colony. However, because of health and climate, they finally settled in the city of Cochabamba. This was the second largest city in Bolivia, high in the Andean plateau, south of the capitol city of LaPaz. Cochabamba is a center for several mission organizations, and soon many missionaries, as well as nationals, were seeking Dr. Johnson s care. And here the Johnsons spent the rest of their lives together.

When they arrived in Cochabamba in 1946, the streets were cobblestone, made of large round rocks cemented together in such a rough fashion that it was extremely difficult for an able bodied person to walk on them. Dorothy found it impossible BUT   GOD! Within one year the city repaved every street. As Dorothy related later, it was just like the Lord to have the streets smoothed to make it possible for her to get around.

Timothy Johnson

In 1949, a young mother was very sick and unable to care for her newborn baby. The Johnsons adopted the Bolivian Indian boy and named him Timothy. He was their only child.

Expanded Ministry Quarters

After visiting the C.C.A. office in North Dakota in 1958, the Johnsons attended the annual Christian Chiropractors Association convention in Davenport, Iowa, in August 1958 and shared their work in Bolivia. The C.C.A. members were moved to raise funds to send chiropractic equipment to Bolivia just as we had for the Thompsons in Ethiopia. In fact, Dr. R. N. Thompson was one of the first to contribute to the new Operation Bolivia project.

One year later, on August 7, 1959, as the Christian Chiropractors Association was having its annual convention in Colorado Springs, Colorado, the Johnsons boarded a ship for South America. On that ship was a full-spine adjusting table donated by Mr. William Lorang of Williams Manufacturing Co. of Elgin, Illinois. (Over the years Mr. Lorang donated several more adjusting tables to C.C.A. missionaries.) Also on board were various other pieces of clinic and laboratory equipment, an X-ray machine with all of the accessories, and a brand new Dodge Power Wagon.

Meanwhile, their sponsoring church in Philadelphia decided to purchase a large two story house on the southern outskirts of Cocha-bamba to serve as mission headquarters, church, home, and clinic for the Johnson s chiro-practic ministry.

Johnson s Home, Clinic & Mission Headquarters

When the Johnsons moved into their new two-story home and clinic, they realized that the house stood about 100 yards off a major high-way. That was great for access and for quietness, but they did not want anyone else building something which would obstruct their access. They immediately put out a call to get help to buy that lot.

On June 26th, 1959, C.C.A. members Drs. Arthur and Esther Mork, lost their fifteen-year-old daughter Charlene of Janesville, Wisconsin, in an automobile accident. Drs. Arthur and Esther chose to establish a memorial in in the name of their beloved daughter to help purchase that lot for the Johnsons.

Mrs. Mork wrote at that time, W e want to know that a small plot of ground in Bolivia, South America, might help some child to know Jesus Christ because a child in the U.S.A. has gone to be with Jesus. This became known as the Charlene Mork Memorial Project.

Palmer School of Chiropractic, where the Morks went to school, joined C.C.A. in promoting the project throughout the chiropractic profession. Funds came from chiropractors everywhere. The Johnsons were able to not only purchase the empty lot but also build a chapel on the lot. The entire project was dedicated in memory of Charlene Mork, and Dr. Esther Mork went to Bolivia for that dedication.

Dorothy was always very involved in the ministry, but this magnificent new home, clinic, mission headquarters presented the problem of how to get to the second floor? Remember, Dorothy had braces on her legs and used crutches to walk. Level ground

Charlene Mork

was a challenge; climbing steps was extremely difficult. The only steps to the second floor living quarters were on the outside, and Dorothy must navigate up and down those steps several times every day. How she prayed for an elevator. But the price made it seem like an impossible wish BUT GOD!!

Then in 1965, when the Johnsons were on furlough, they visited Mr. and Mrs. Jim Wallace of Pennsylvania. Mrs. Wallace also had polio and was confined to a wheel chair, and Mr. Wallace had built an elevator to help his wife get upstairs in their home. Mr. Wallace offered to build one for Dorothy, provided workers could be found in Bolivia to assemble it. The Johnsons found necessary help, and the Christian Chiropractors Association paid for the shipping. What a joy and help it was for Dorothy to have that elevator.

The First Chiropractic License in South America

It is believed that when Dr. J. Bridgens Johnson arrived in Peru in 1938 he became the first chiropractor to practice in South America. With the new clinic and C.C.A.-provided equipment, Dr. Bridge s ministry expanded and he felt he should seek official status. In 1960 he became the first chiropractor to receive a license to practice chiropractic in South America, at which time the National Chiropractic Association labeled him The Lone Ranger of South America. He traveled to LaPaz, the capitol of Bolivia, to get his license and detailed the process in the following letter dated September 26, 1960:

"I arrived in LaPaz at 10 o'clock on Tuesday night, and I knew I could do nothing about the license until morning. In the morning I went to the lawyer, and...he suggested I take diplomas and documents to the American Embassy to have them certified, as this would be the first requirement of Bolivian government.

"[The American Embassy] refused absolutely to certify them. The man said he could certify that I was an American citizen by my passport, but that he knew nothing whatsoever of any of the schools I attended. He suggested...[that I] send each paper home to somebody in the States...and have somebody get a certified statement from a notary or someone responsible for declaring genuineness of schools...

"I went back to the lawyer. He was a bit huffed and said if the ambassador didn't want to help, we would get along without his help. He told me to leave all the papers there that night...and come back the next morning...He would do the best he could.

"First [a couple of courts had] to authorize a couple of men

whom we designated as translators to translate all documents into Spanish. This being done, the translators had to return to court and swear that they had been properly translated, after which they recommended them to the attention of the Minister of Education.

"The Director of Education added a note to the affect that since...chiropractic has never existed in Bolivia, the Minister of Education should make a full study of my documents...and possibly recommend full revalidation of existing U.S. Titles...especially since it was to be done in association with the gospel work here in Bolivia.

"I then went to the Minister of Education himself, who was very slow to act, but my lawyer just kept running into his office until he gave him a definite time it would be ready...At that time the lawyer and I went to his office. We didn't see the Minister himself, but his chief official greeted us as we came in and told us everything was ready. [He] showed us...that the Minister himself had added a note that it had been resolved to fully recognize and validate my title duly issued by established institutions in the U.S. and that I was fully authorized to practice my profession, Doctor of Chiropractic, here in Bolivia. His signature and seal were attached.

"The official Mayor suggested I [wait in his office] while the lawyer took it around to a few other offices and had it fully registered in official archives of each office after which he brought it back to the desk of the official. [The Mayor then] handed it to me, took me by the hand, and said 'from this day on [you are] free to practice...in Bolivia without any fear of being molested from any source, professional, or authority, either city, state, or national, as [you are] now being given full recognition by the government.

"After thanking him, the lawyer and I left his office. The lawyer was rejoicing as much as I was about what had taken place. Then he said [he wanted to take me to] the Minister of Relations Exterior and Culture....[The lawyer] showed [the Minister] the document we had received and told him that he wanted to have it legalized...so that it would have official reciprocity throughout all of South America. The Minister said he would be glad to do that, after which he signed and sealed and registered it fully in his archives.

"[The lawyer then explained] that if I ever had to go to another country where they had this professional reciprocity, I would just have to make one registration to have my professional standing here transferred. He even said that some of the states at

home had the same professional reciprocity with Bolivia, which
would make it easier to get my license at home through this."

Thus Dr. Bridgens Johnson received legal recognition for himself
and for his profession in Bolivia and never had any legal problems
with the government or the medical profession as long as he practiced
in Bolivia.

Dr. Stan Lindblom's Short-Term Ministry

August 1, 1965, Dr. Stan Lindblom of Plentywood, Montana, wrote
C.C.A. indicating that he would like to work with the Johnsons in Bolivia for a short term. Dr. Lindblom's brother had joined his practice
in Plentywood, and, as Dr. Lindblom was single and had no family
obligations, he felt the call to serve the Lord in short-term chiropractic
missions. He had already worked with Dr. Dinah Van Dyken for a
brief period in Window Rock, Arizona, and his appetite was whetted
for more mission activity.

Dr. Lindblom left Montana on September 27th and arrived in
Cochabamba on September 29th. He took a taxi to the home of the
Johnsons because they had not received the letter indicating when he
was to arrive. (The letter arrived after Dr. Lindblom got there.)

On October 5th, 1965, Dr. Lindblom wrote:

"The Johnsons have...made me feel right at home. This is
a very nice place, Glenn, and we can be proud that the C.C.A.
has people such as the Johnsons to represent them here. He
has a very nice practice, and they are very busy in the mission
church work and Sunday school, which both have a large
attendance with very dedicated Christian people assisting them."

The admiration went both ways. Dr. Bridge enjoyed discussing
various cases and new techniques with Dr. Stan, and Dr. Stan helped
the Johnsons expand the work into the country. Dorothy wrote that
Dr. Stan endeared himself to everyone–missionaries, Bolivian Christians, high-class folk, and the humble ones. He showed God's love
through chiropractic adjustments, advice, prayer, and singing in the
choir.

Dorothy also felt that this good-looking bachelor needed a wife,
and when Dorothy sets her mind to something, you can be sure it gets
done. A good friend of the Johnsons, Lillian Kvamsdal had been a
missionary in Bolivia with World Mission Prayer League since 1949,
working first in the lowlands and then in LaPaz, primarily in children's

ministries and in orphanages. When she visited Cochabamba, Dorothy wasted no time introducing Lillian to Dr. Stan. *(For more on Dr. Lindblom's ministry and on Dorothy's matchmaking, see the chapter on Dr. Stanley Lindblom)* On January 4, 1969, Lillian and Stan were married in Swea City, Iowa. Dorothy wrote the following:

> *"I am sure you are all very happy about Stan's decision to get married to a real wonderful girl. All right, I'm cupid!"*

The Final Years

In January 1968 Dr. Glenn Stillwagon and I were privileged to spend a week with the Johnsons in Cochabamba. It was a tremendous experience and one which we still remember with great joy and satisfaction. (More about this trip in the World Tour of Missions chapter.)

After the dedication of the new chapel in May 1971, the church moved out of the Johnsons two story home. The entire first floor was converted into a chiropractic clinic with a reception area, private office, two adjusting rooms, bathroom, and an office for a dentist who was a member of the Johnson's church. The entire second floor was then transformed into living area.

In March 1977, Dorothy became increasingly ill, and it was soon apparent that she was not able to carry on with the mission responsibilities. She was in and out of the hospital, and she was no longer able to go to her upstairs living quarters. When the Johnsons had built the chapel, they included a parsonage for the Bolivian pastor; however, they were never able to complete it. They now finished it quickly and moved Dorothy into it. For several months she was unable to even get out of bed.

She rallied somewhat during the summer of 1978, and they decided to leave Bolivia for good. They turned over the chapel and parsonage to a Plymouth Brethren Assembly, and Tim stayed on in the house. The X-ray equipment and some of the other clinic supplies were sold, and the Johnsons returned to the U.S. on July 8, 1978. Dorothy was taken to a hospital and then into a nursing home in Reading, Pennsylvania, where she stayed until she died on July 18, 1980. In April 1984, Dr. Bridge was diagnosed with leukemia, and he died about six months later.

Dr. Bridgens and Dorothy Johnson accomplished much in Bolivia during their 45+ years of ministry. Many would say it was against all odds...BUT GOD.

Lebanon, Qatar, Iran
Dr. Flora Hill Colby

Dr. Flora Hill Colby ministered as an independent Assembly of God missionary in conjunction with the Christian Chiropractors Association in several Middle Eastern countries from 1947-1979. She had a particular concern for mentally and physically handicapped children with a special call from God to go to the Arabic people.

Ministry in Lebanon

In 1947 Rev. Ralph Colby and Dr. Flora Hill Colby opened a small children's clinic in Lebanon and started a mission. A 9x12 foot room housed Dr. Colby's clinic during the week and their church on Sunday. In 1949 Dr. Flora became very ill, and they had to return to the U.S. The Colbys, however, returned to Lebanon the next year and soon had a larger facility for their mission. Before long they had started six churches in Beruit and five missions in other Lebanese villages.

Dr. Flora Hill Colby

During most of her time in Lebanon, Dr. Colby used her chiropractic training to support herself as an independent missionary. Lebanon did not recognize any health profession other than medical physicians, but God opened the door for Dr. Colby to minister to some influential families:

> *"God gave me special favor in that I was able to accomplish some extra ordinary results among the families of the 'powers that be' at the very beginning. They recognized the value of the chiropractic profession in their country, and so with much pressure, I have been able to maintain at least as much as I could handle with my many other duties. I thank God it has been a real door of effectual contact."* (Oct. 22, 1960)

In August 1959 Rev. and Dr. Colby returned to the U.S. on furlough. While they were home, their mission board decided to replace them with a younger couple and chose not to continue the Colby's support. Even without her mission's support, Dr. Colby decided to return to Lebanon; however, she wrote, "I do not have the strength to carry on a full time practice any more, and to also do the necessary work of a mission station." At age 59, Dr. Colby feared she was working against all odds...BUT GOD. Dr. Colby continued for another 20 years!

When Dr. Colby returned to Lebanon in 1960, Rev. Colby stayed in California to help support her ministry. The Christian Chiropractors Association arranged for her to take an X-ray machine, a hi-lo manual adjusting table, a side posture table, several analytical instruments, and miscellaneous pieces of professional equipment to help in her chiropractic practice. She wrote later:

> "I sincerely thank God for the C.C.A. and you very able leaders who are so truly consecrated both to God and your principles and express the courage of your convictions. I shall do my utmost to be worthy always of the 'so great a gift of salvation from my Lord' and also to prove myself worthy of the trust and confidence expressed by my fellow laborers for a needy world."

Dr. Flora had a unique way of reaching to the lowest of society as well as to its highest members. Several Lebanese government officials received chiropractic care from her including the daughter of the Prime Minister. Many new converts were sponsored through school by Dr. Flora including a medical doctor in Beirut, two international evangelists, the head of the synod of the Presbyterian Church of Lebanon, and a Syrian pastor serving in Australia. All of these were converts through the ministry of Dr. Colby.

Ministry in Qatar

While in Beirut, Dr. Colby treated the Down syndrome son of a Lebanese businessman who was general manager for a large importing company stationed in Doha, Qatar, on the Arabian Gulf. Qatar is an Arab sheikdom, formerly known as a slave trading site but more recently as an oil rich kingdom. This total Muslim state was essentially closed to all except Muslim visitors. Christians were not allowed in the country under penalty of death. As the oil industry developed, these conditions were relaxed somewhat, but when Dr. Colby was invited in 1966, it was still a very closed country. Getting into Qatar was against all odds...BUT GOD! At the time of her call to Qatar, Dr. Colby wrote the following letters:

> _May 27, 1966_ "I think what I am about to tell you will come as a surprise, but believe me, I am absolutely sure it is God's perfect will for me. I want to go to the eastern coasts of Arabia to carry on my combined chiropractic and missionary work. The area will be either Qatar or Abu Dhabi. I trust later to hold both sides of the Arabian Gulf.

"I much prefer to start in Doha, the capitol of Qatar with a population of 45,000 including 250 families of foreigners, as it is more modernized and certainly easier to get started in and adjusted to climate and all things in general. Besides, I have very good contacts now there, and I think it will not be too difficult to get started. So I want to launch out for the C.C.A. and open another frontier for someone else to follow me a bit later.

"I know God has called me, and I know He will hold me as long as there is something left undone of my particular work that He has set aside for me to do. I am very anxious to go and hope to go down in two weeks for four days to check with the government and to size up things in general.

"It is impossible to get into the country even for a visit unless someone already there makes a written request called a 'no objections certificate' for your presence there. Fortunately God has been very gracious to me and taken care of that item.

"It is not possible for anyone to get into the country as a missionary, but I can get in as a doctor. After I am there, I will be able to hold services in my house even as I do here. Just recently they permitted one Catholic priest and one Protestant minister to enter the country once each week for the sake of the foreigners, but they must do their praying in the homes–no public service is as yet allowed. But I am trusting that many souls may find Christ as their Savior as my distribution of literature from my clinic will go on just the same as it does here.

"In my spare time I trust I shall be able to reach some of the Bedouins on the outside. I am thrilled beyond words because my call was originally to that area of Arabia, but for various reasons, including the fact of no admittance, I was not able to go on from here.

"If this is a bit incoherent don't mind, and I will try to do better next time. When you are housemother to a school of [mentally handicapped students while being] a doctor and a missionary and other items too numerous to mention, it takes a bit of doing and a LOT of time.

"Also I am allergic to so many things. Almost any drug throws my muscles into spasms. But I am better, and God is undertaking in a very special way. But please do pray for me. I know I shall be completely well when I have taken the final step toward doing the work the Lord called me to do so many years ago. He is faithful.

"A note of praise is due here–you will remember that I have had gangrene in my feet from hyper-insulinism for several *years–nearly lost the left one twice in the past three years. Well, three weeks ago God completely healed me from that, and what a great, great blessing!!!*

June 18, 1966 "Greetings in Jesus Name from the Arabian Gulf States...I am very thankful that I took this trip. Now I know what I am coming into, and it is much better. I think it is best that I retain a small place in Beirut and plan to go back for the three hottest months. It is too hot for me I think in the summer, even though the house is airconditioned. One cannot spend the entire time indoors.

"I am thrilled beyond words at the opportunities I shall have here, and I plan to return to Doha in November at the latest. I am definitely sure here lies my greatest avenue of service for my Lord and my profession. Do pray for me and for all wisdom. Yours in the bonds of Calvary, Flora."

At that time Doha, Qatar, was a city of 45,000 people on a small peninsula off the eastern coast of Arabia in the Arabian Gulf. It was 100% Moslem with 120 mosques and no Christian churches. Later that fall, Dr. Flora wrote the following:

"Greetings from Doha in the matchless Name of Jesus our risen Lord and Savior. How wonderful to know Him and to have the light of the Gospel shine into our hearts. I am so happy to be able to tell you that [yesterday] I received the adjusting table that you sent. It is beautiful and wonderful in every way, and I am so very grateful to everyone who had a part in it. Surely it will be used to the glory of God and the good of man. Thank you all so much, and may God reward you richly in every way. I used it twice today–once for a tiny Muslim boy 10 months old who had polio and again for a man with muscular contractions.

"Truly I praise God for His wonderful guiding and keeping power and that He never fails us and His promises are yea and amen. I thank Him for the privilege, and that He has counted me worthy to be a carrier of His glorious Gospel. I pray I may be but an empty, clean channel through which the water of life may flow to others. All I ask is that many of these haunting eyes and sad faces may be enlightened because I have been able to give just a little in return for the great load lifted from my own life in knowing Him whom to know is life eternal. Thank God.

"It would be impossible for me to describe the loneliness of this place, and I thank God now that He has prepared me somewhat for it in the past few years. I am alone except for the two little dogs I brought with me from Lebanon. They help a lot– no Christian service of any kind these three weeks.

"I hope to start a Bible study as soon as I get furniture and restore two souls to His fellowship. One is a head nurse in the hospital who had grown very cold and distant after 8-1/2 years here. She says she feels a great load lifted and a dark veil lifted from her heart and eyes. I also want to reach out to the man who did some electrical work for me. I know there are many waiting. Pray I may never fail in one iota. It seems it was not as easy as it seemed and very heavy opposition arose to my being here. BUT GOD ... is on our side." (Flora Colby, Nov. 1966)

For several years Dr. Colby's friendship to the ruling sheik caused the powers that be to look the other way, and although she was very discreet in her Gospel work, her church was open to the public. Ostensibly it was to serve the many Indian and Pakistani people who were living in the country working in the banking and petroleum businesses. Dr. Glenn Stillwagon of Monongahela, Pennsylvania, Dr. Harry Kalsbeek of Castro Valley, California, and I visited with Dr. Colby in Doha, Qatar, in February, 1968.

That summer, however, Dr. Colby began having trouble with the government officials. An extension on her visa was repeatedly refused and her friends were unable to help her. The hospital in Doha had taken on a physical therapist, and they were discouraging patients from going to Dr. Flora. Dr. Flora saw this as an attempt to shut down her Christian witness in that land.

Ministry In Iran

In September 1968, Dr. Colby moved to Shiraz, Iran, opening a clinic and establishing a Bible study program and church. She also worked with a psychologist who was a professor at the University and had his own mental hospital with 82 mentally handicapped children. She reported that the six-year-old grandson of the doctor had been able to walk for the first time after 13 adjustments. He had been taken to specialists in Europe and the U.S. without success.

Shiraz was only 45 minutes by air across the Arabian Gulf from Doha, and Dr. Flora was able to return to Qatar for short visits to disciple her Christian friends there.

In 1971 Dr. Flora moved to Tehran, Iran, to work in the J. F. Kennedy Rehabilitation Center for Retarded Children. The Center was developed and supported by a family of nineteen medical doctors with no government support and had a waiting list of over 16,000 patients. When the Center built a hospital addition with much better equipment, a special suite was designed for Dr. Colby.

She received no pay for the work she did at the Center, but at age 70, she was still adjusting up to 30 patients a day with amazing results. She reported that one blind child received her sight, and a total invalid started walking, writing, and could study again. Another patient, a Southern Baptist missionary's young son who was considered mentally handicapped and had a speech difficulty, was able to return to school and was doing well. After Dr. Colby left, Dr. Harry Kalsbeek continued the work in the Center for a year. (More about Dr. Kalsbeek's ministry in another chapter.)

In addition to her work with the Center, Dr. Flora led many women to the Lord through a weekly Bible study. She also ministered among the 15,000 Americans who were living in Iran.

In December 1972, Dr. Colby was forced to move out of Iran because of her health. The climate and altitude of Tehran was too much for her. Her next stop was Jerusalem from where she wrote the following:

"I came to Jerusalem on Dec. 21. I have not been able to start work both from the point of visa and also I have not been strong enough yet, although God has been so very gracious to me. I am at least seventy-five percent better than I was before, and I am gaining ground steadily with only occasional setbacks.

"The Ministry of Interior has promised [to] give me a one year residence visa, and they are processing it now. I have been sponsored by the Chief Medical Officer for the Mentally Retarded for Israel and also the head of the center where I will work. She is a Jewish lady doctor, and she has signed for me. I saw her again a couple of days ago, and she seems very anxious for me to start. I also am anxious as this center cares for all ages up through the fifties and will give me a good chance to show what chiropractic can do for them.

"I like it very much here, and the altitude and climate seem to suit me much better than Iran. I loved it so much there and have missed my work at the Center and all so very much.

"May God continue to bless our profession and each one who labors for God's cause and the betterment of His little ones. Yours for the cause of Christ and Chiropractic, Always, Flora Colby" (Flora Colby, March 1973)

Age and health problems forced Dr. Colby to leave her ministry to the Arabic-speaking people in Jerusalem in 1979 and return to the United States. She died in 1981 at the age of 80. Dr. Flora Colby had ministered in Middle Eastern countries seemingly against all odds...BUT GOD.

Mexico
Dr. and Mrs. Lester Blank

Dr. Lester Blank of Elizabethtown, Pennsylvania and his wife MaryLou of Davenport, Iowa, arrived in Cuba on June 1, 1959, to serve as missionaries for the Franconia Mennonite Board of Missions just five months after Castro had taken over that country. In October 1960 their eldest son, Nelson, was born in Cuba joining their two daughters, Beverly Jean and Carol June.

MaryLou, a registered nurse, was the daughter of Rev. and Mrs. William Lauver, Mennonite missionaries in Argentina for 24 years. Dr. Lester had graduated from Palmer School of Chiropractic in 1953 and had studied at Columbia College of Chiropractic in New York, John Hopkins University, Easter Mennonite College and Elizabethtown College.

Dr. Lester and MaryLou sought to develop a health ministry and mission outreach to the Cuban people, but their eventual goal was to serve among the Indian tribes of South Central Mexico. One of their main purposes for going to Cuba was language study. Dr. Blank tells of his first few months in Cuba and having to write out his sermons because of his limited knowledge of Spanish.

They left Cuba on December 1, 1960, primarily because U.S. banks were not allowed to transfer money to Cuba and the Blanks had no way to receive their financial assistance. Dr. Blank reported that there had been no opposition to their work, and that they had been treated very courteously and respectfully during their almost two years in Cuba.

The Blank Family: top row - Nelson, Beverly, Carol, Keith seated - Miriam, Mary Lou, Dr. Lester, Paul

Beginning the Ministry in Mexico

Dr. Lester was ordained into the ministry on September 10, 1961. After taking a Bible translation course at the Wycliffe Summer Institutes of Linguistics, the Blanks headed for South Central Mexico. There they served for 10 years with the Trique Indians high in mountains. During that time, Wycliffe translators completed the New Testament in the Trique language, but Dr. Lester discovered that it was seldom used.

"Although the Trique New Testament has been in circulation for two years now (1972), yet it is being used by only a very few people. There are several reasons for this:

1) The Trique society is not a reading people. That is, they have not been reading for past centuries. Only in the last 30 to 40 years were some of them able to read some Spanish. Reading is not a habit for them as a people.

2) The only reading material available to them has been Spanish, a language that is not native to them, hence the comprehension in Spanish is limited.

3) The only literates among them have been taught to read in the public school system in Spanish. The Trique alphabet has a few more letters and diacritical tone marks, which alphabet was phonetically and scientifically developed by the Wycliffe Bible translators. Many Triques seem to feel that the extra marks in their language make it to hard to read. Actually this is not so, since a few have learned to read Trique quite well in a short time.

"We want to encourage learning to read Trique by making more simple reading materials in Trique. Then they will be able to read the Trique New Testament and their comprehension will be nearly 100%, because it is in their own mother tongue. In the meantime, we continue to show Gospel film strips two nights a week and the script on the tape recorder speaks their own language read directly from the Trique New Testament.

"This month was a highlight for us. The first Trique believer from our local area was baptized in a stream near Tlaxiaco, along with five other believers in the Tlaxiaco area. Rejoice with us in the Lord. May His Spirit so work that this will be the first fruits of the harvest in Trique land.

"A major block of our time is still dedicated to caring for those who are sick or injured. This aspect of our work seems to be the most appreciated. Whenever we need to make trips into Mexico City for a week or more, the Triques invariably say, 'What will we do for our sickness and injuries? We'll all die before you return!' Obviously this is greatly exaggerated, but it reveals one of our major roles in their thinking." (Lester Blank, March 1972)

Life among the Trique Indians was very primitive. The Blanks lived in a one-room, hand-hewn log house with a loft for their bedrooms. The home had a thatched roof with a brick tiled floor. Dr. Lester's clinic was in the entryway of the house. Everything, including the furniture, table and chairs, and kitchen sink, were hand made.

Dr. Lester, MaryLou, and their six children (Carole, Beverly, Nelson, Miriam, Keith, and Paul) called this log house "home" for the years of their service there. Housekeeping was a tremendous job. The nearest electricity was thirty-five miles away, and the only running water was a spring on the hillside a quarter mile away.

The Indians themselves were friendly but very shy and superstitious. They depended on Dr. Blank for most of their daily sustenance, from buying their eggs and produce, changing their money, taking care of their sicknesses and injuries, and serving as arbitrator in time of

The Lester Blank family in front of their mission home.

trouble, arguments, and disagreements. Dr. Lester relates that when he first started giving adjustments to the Indians, he found that they were familiar with what he wanted them to do because they had three or four old "bone-setter men" in the tribal area who did some form of manipulation. However, he states that he never was able to observe them at work.

Continuing the Ministry Part-time

The school for the Indian children had only grades one and two, with a teacher who had only an eighth grade education. For a number of years MaryLou Blank home schooled their children and four other missionary children with correspondence courses. Because of the educational needs of their six children, the Blanks resigned as full time missionaries in 1972. Dr. Lester took over the chiropractic practice of his father, Dr. Aaron Blank, in Gap, Pennsylvania, and he continued in that practice until his retirement many years later. However, each summer they returned to Mexico for several weeks' ministry with the Trique Indians. Dr. Lester wrote the following account of that ministry:

"As you know, four years ago we terminated full time service with the Mennonite Mission Board, but have returned each summer for a short term of summer missionary teaching service to the same community where we lived those 10 years before. Even though we feel it is God's will for the present that we be here in the U.S., we are happy that we can return each summer for concentrated Bible studies with the Triques.

"By concentrating our time and energies together with long days, we estimate that we get about three times the amount done during that month that we are here. This is true because not only do we know our time is limited but so do our Trique friends. They come for adjustments in increased numbers and regularly for Bible study every night of the month we are there.

"During the summer of 1974, several requested water baptism. This was the first baptism ever held there. (Two other Trique believers had been baptized previously but not in the Trique communities.) They're ten promising young men who publicly gave their vows before the Lord and demonstrated their faith publicly by baptism. It was a great day of rejoicing for us and for them! What joy radiated from their faces. Theirs was no small decision! Possible persecution and certain ridicule awaited them. But they have remained faithful to the Lord and His Word! Praise the Lord!

"This past summer of 1975 found us again in Trique land. Again we were busy giving adjustments, preparing Bible lessons, and teaching each evening. Imagine our joy when again there was a request for another baptism for fourteen more believers...four more men and ten women. We praise God for His Spirit's working in their hearts and making His Word real to them. Truly it is God's doing and it is marvelous in our eyes. Praise His Name." (Lester Blank, Dec.1975)

In 1982 Dr. Lester preached in the first Trique Indian church. What a joy it was to realize that their years of service in this remote part of South Central Mexico had finally brought into existence a church the Trique Indians could call their own. It was against all odds–primitive living conditions, illiteracy, and superstition–But God!

Operation Navajo
Dr. Dinah VanDyken

Dinah VanDyken was born in Montana, one of ten children. Her family moved to California when she was ten years old, where she grew up, went to high school, and then on to nursing school.

In 1938 she was invited to go to the Navajo Reservation as a missionary nurse with the Christian Reformed Mission Board. She spent two years on that assignment and returned to California to attend Bible college. In 1949 she returned to spend another two and a half years at the Navajo mission hospital where her sister was a nurse.

Dr. Dinah VanDyken

Answering the Call to Minister

As far back as 1938 Dinah had wanted to go to chiropractic college; finally in the mid-1950s, this became a reality. She graduated from Cleveland Chiropractic College in Los Angeles in 1957. She had long felt a call to serve the Navajo Indians in Arizona and New Mexico, and with her chiropractic training, she felt the Lord calling her to this field with an even greater opportunity for service:

> *"The Navajo tribe is the largest Indian tribe in our land. They are scattered over quite a large reservation. Many have seen few white people, and what they see puzzles them, as some come with the Gospel while others seek to lead them into greater sin and more darkness than they had already known. Since I already have the confidence of some of the Navajos, and can begin to use their language, I am looking forward to great things for the Lord, with His indispensable blessing."* (Dinah VanDyken, 1959)

In March 1959 the Christian Chiropractors Association became aware of her call and offered to support her ministry. Over the next couple of years, the C.C.A. arranged for an X-ray machine, a new adjusting table (donated by Williams Manufacturing Co. in Elgin, IL), some laboratory equipment, and other miscellaneous equipment to be shipped to her home/office in Window Rock, Arizona. The C.C.A. also applied for non-profit corporation status in New Mexico to set up the "Operation Navajo" project to support this ministry. Dr. Dinah entered language school to learn the Navajo language, and at the same time took her Board exams to get a chiropractic license in both Arizona and New Mexico.

Dr. Dinah lived and practiced for the next several years in a home and office combination just east of Window Rock, Arizona. As a single woman, she encountered many problems trying to keep equipment running and deal with poorly constructed homes, poor roads, and severe winters. But the Navajos were receptive to chiropractic care, and she continued a ministry in this very difficult field.

In her November 1962 newsletter, Dr. Dinah wrote of some of her victories and her trials:

"I left some 'seed' in six homes one Sunday afternoon. On the next call there, Grandma Sadie, who is over 100 years old, seemed changed. As I started to read the Navajo of 'Jesus Loves Me,' her face lit up with joy and she said, 'I love that Jesus too!' I had planned my song schedule, but changed it. We sang 'O Happy Day, That Fixed My Choice on Thee, My Savior and My God.'

"Another lady in the home is showing interest as well. Also an aged blind couple, medicine man and his wife, welcome visits and are willing to listen to God's Word. I have seen reverent attention to God's Word in homes of my Sunday School preschoolers, with prayer requests often. Four-year-old Adeline whispered to me in church, just as the pastor started to pray, 'He ought to pray for my Grandma.' Why, I asked, 'Grandma is sick.'

"In order that the Operation Navajo mission may truly be 'to the praise of His glory,' I urgently request that you pray with me for courage and steadfastness. When discouragement hits me, I often wonder, 'has everyone forgotten to pray?' I have received reports that a false religious group in this area has warned people to avoid my place. However, one man from the midst of their group has seen the Light and become a member of a local Baptist mission.

"Liquor among the Navajos is causing untold misery, many deaths, and horrible neglect of little ones and aged folks. Yesterday a sheriff stopped by and told me he had found a small child's body rotted to death from neglect by alcoholic parents. Please pray for the Navajos.

"Other lesser problems [include the following]: Many who have shared the burden of support have let it slide lately. Pa-

tients promise to pay me, and the promise dies without paying. My water system froze last December and still isn't normal. My roof is no good when it rains, and the landlord refuses to fix it. Land was offered for a permanent location, but several hundred feet of access road would be required to reach the property from the highway. Please continue to pray."

Welcoming Help

Dr. Stan Lindblom, a C.C.A. member from Plentywood, Montana, went to work with Dr. Dinah for several weeks in the summer of 1965, allowing Dr. Dinah to take a much-needed vacation. Dr. Lindblom wrote from Window Rock in July 1965:

"Greetings from Navajoland...We had a good trip down and have been working with Dr. Dinah. I have learned much about the Navajo people and the problems concerning the lives of these people which are many, and with these people, progress moves slowly as with many of the reservations. Customs, beliefs, habits, and certain outside groups which are not helping, make this so.

"Dinah has done quite a bit of work here with this place, and I have been doing just about everything since I came here— yard cleaning, lab work, pounding nails, repairing some of the equipment, milking the goat, etc. We are still waiting for the X-ray equipment man to get over here from Albuquerque. He comes to Gallup about every three weeks to the...local hospital to check their machines...Dr Dinah wrote to him at Albuquerque asking him to stop over. I believe the trouble is in the transformer or tube—it doesn't sound right when contact is engaged, and we did not want to run it too much and possibly induce further damage. Also it seems to get hot. I can see other things that make the work here difficult which I will fill you in on later.

"Dr. Dinah still plans strongly for a home for the aged. She has opportunity to get a good piece of ground and at not too bad a price at the junction of the highway at Gallup/Window Rock intersection, about a half mile down the road from here.

"As I have been on the board of directors of the rest home at Wolf Point for five years from inception till it was finished, I listed all the things that were necessary before one even broke ground, which are many. This rather surprised her, so we looked into a few things I suggested, and it showed what was necessary. There is a great need for a home such as this, and the welfare and caseworkers were all for it. I have been in some of the hogans and seen some of these old people, Glenn, and I could hardly believe such conditions.

"In the meantime, we also looked at a couple of places in Gallup. I feel that she would be much better off to make the move, as the property owners here, I believe, want to set up a new Christian radio station here which they are planning and working towards. We are going to look some more when she gets back from a family reunion in California.

"I have been taking care of things here for her. I can't take care of any patients because I do not have a license here, but I have been taking care of lab work and the goats, etc. I was staying in town at a little apartment owned by a fine Christian family but have moved out here while she is gone as there are too many Indians wandering about day and night, which is a problem here.

"There is a very nice interdenominational Christian mission here which we attend–church, Bible study and meetings–some very fine Christian workers and missionaries there. On Sunday we pick up a load of children out over the reservation and take them in. Their parents are not Christians, although a couple of the mothers are more interested all the time.

"I must close now and may the Lord bless you all in your home and your activities. Sincerely in Christ, Stan M. Lindblom"

In September 1965, Dr. Dinah wrote expressing her appreciation for Dr. Lindblom's assistance:

"I want to express by thanks and praise to the Lord and my deep appreciation to Dr. Stanley Lindblom for the help, encouragement, and fellowship in the Lord during Dr. Stan's recent visit.

"The Navajos felt at home with him, as he has a quiet way that appeals to them. His genuine interest in them and their welfare could be felt. I feel, if the Lord ever removes me from this work before we have a Christian Navajo Chiropractor, Dr. Stan would be able to take over very nicely as my replacement. Missionaries here also felt drawn to him."

Moving the Ministry

In February 1966, Dr. VanDyken moved from the difficult situation she had in Window Rock into Gallup, New Mexico. Gallup was a little larger town and was a commercial center for the Navajos. In Gallup, she rented a nice 10-room home, large enough for her clinic and living quarters, and a second floor which she rented out for additional income. In the city, her opportunities for ministry increased substantially.

"I have many new avenues for service. I have placed tracts in several strategic places around town and one supermarket owner gave me permission to distribute tracts to his patrons every Saturday night.

> *"I have a Good News Club for neighborhood children on Mondays and a small beginning of a class for mothers as well. I have been visiting in neighbor homes. Children are coming to my home for personal Bible study. A truckload of Navajos waved and honked as they drove by. I also have some new challenges: handicapped children are very numerous.*
>
> *"Would the Lord send another chiropractor to Operation Navajo Mission so we can go out by turns and reach them out on the reservation? Older Navajos have many chronic ailments also."* (Dinah VanDyken, July 1966)

In June 1970, Dr. Dinah needed to return to Ripon, California, to care for ailing members of her family. At the same time, another Christian chiropractor, Dr. Frank Alstrin, got his license to practice in New Mexico and took over Dr. Dinah's practice. He was not a missionary but did continue a Christian witness through his practice in Gallup. Dr. Dinah, therefore, took "a leave of absence" from her life-long calling of work with the Navajo Indians of New Mexico and Arizona.

Although Dr. Dinah had the responsibility of caring for her parents and her sister, she later entered into a special ministry to shut-ins, especially those confined to the rest homes in her area. She would take her guitar and Bible and sing to and teach those who had no opportunity to hear the Word of God in any other way.

Operation Navajo
Dr. and Mrs. Frank Alstrin

When Dr. Dinah Van Dyken retired from her ministry to the Navajo Indians, Dr. Frank Alstrin, a young graduate of the Palmer College of Chiropractic stepped up to take over her work. Soon after moving into the home and office formerly occupied by Dr. Van Dyken, Dr. Frank married Suzann Scott, a young lady he met in Gallup, New Mexico, where he was ministering.

As Dr. Frank continued to learn the Navajo language, his primary outreach was to the children in the slums of Gallup . The Navajos gradually accepted him and Susan, and the Alstrins continued their ministry until January 1975 when they moved to California.

Peru
Dr. and Mrs. Larry Garman

The ministry of Dr. Larry and Addie Garman and their four children is one of the most outstanding of any that we have to report. They established over 200 hundred churches with thousands of believers along the upper tributaries of the Amazon and Maranon rivers in northern Peru. They started Bible schools and training schools in several locations. They treated all kinds of musculo-skeletal problems like typical American chiropractors, but also extracted teeth and treated tropical diseases, snake-bites, burns, and fractures. They offered

Dr. Larry Garman

the only health service for many miles around, and almost anything could happen.

Trip to the Mission

Dr. Larry Garman graduated from Los Angeles College of Chiropractic in 1964, and he and Addie volunteered for missionary service with the Nazarene Church of America. Their mission bought the equipment for and set up a health clinic on the banks of the Amazon River in Peru. Addie, a registered nurse, helped in the clinic outreach. Dr. Garman once described the trip into his mission station home:

"Our station is quite isolated, and there are no roads in our immediate area. We take our supplies with us...for the intended time in the tribe...kerosene, gasoline, petroleum, oil, and food stuffs by truck over the great Andes Mountains and down to where the road ends at a place called Nazareth. From there we...[transfer] the supplies into our mission boat and head down the mighty Maranon River.

"It is a beautiful trip as the current is quite rapid in this, the

Addie Garman, R.N.

headwaters of the Maranon. There are places of danger in the
river depending on the amount of rainfall and how much the river
rises. The jungles in this part of Peru have some elevation to
them, and it is a gorgeous carpet of green that unfolds before
your eyes as you travel down river winding your way through its
course. Before arriving at our station, we pass several
Aguaruna villages, with the typical thatched roofs, and the cane
poles that make up the siding for their houses.

"After several hours, you round a bend in the river and in
the distance you can see the missionary house on the Kusu
station. Pulling into the Kusu River, one notices the difference in
the two rivers. The Kusu is smaller and very tranquil, while the
Maranon is rough and fast. There from the smaller Kusu River,
[we get] a full view of the mission...

"The white house glistening in the sun makes a favorable
impression on one traveling this part of the river. Beside the
house is the washhouse, and on down the walkway we come to
one of the two twin clinic buildings. The first clinic is for storing
medicines and houses our treatment area, along with our
Mussler table and Thompson adjusting tables for giving chiropractic treatments. The other clinic building is for in-patients
who must be kept over night.

"Leaving the clinic area, we go down a hill and up another
to arrive at the new Kusu church, recently constructed with the
help of our Aguaruna Indians. It is a beautiful sight to watch our
people come for Sunday services. With the sun shining over the
tropical rain forest and peeking through the trees with its glim-
mering rays illuminating the ground, one receives a feeling of
warmth from nature and this wonderful creation of God's.

"This is a land of eternal springtime, singing birds, rugged
rolling mountains, swift turbulent rivers, fluffy clouds that quick
as a wink can change into dark threatening storm heads dumping 10 to 15 inches of clear soft water onto an already soaked
land. Ours is a jungle filled with every insect imaginable, exotic
plant life, snakes of many varieties (more than our share of
poisonous ones in these last few months) and [it is] also a
paradise for parasites. We have everything from head lice to
hookworm, from malaria to hideous leishmaniasis.

"The Indians become noticeable as the canoes paddle into
the mission, and others arrive on the trail from yet another
direction. The people come early for church and wait patiently
for the service to begin. We sing in Aguaruna and Spanish, but
the message is translated from Spanish into Aguaruna. We do

not have all the New Testament written in Aruaruna yet, so Bible texts are somewhat limited for memorization work.

"The Lord is blessing, and we love Him more and more. Please pray for revival among the Agurunas. The Lord willing, we will be having a Bible course and young people will come from various parts of the tribe to study with us on the Kusu station. Pray for our young people to accept the call of God to prepare themselves to take the Gospel to their own people."

Life on the Amazon

The river was their main road, and dugout canoe was their primary means of transportation. The river allowed them to travel over many miles of jungle area and establish churches among Aguaruna Indian tribes up and down stream. However, the river also proved to be a problem and at times a hazard.

Dr. Larry tells of the flood in 1971 when they had five feet of water inside their home: the clinic was especially hard hit. They had to live over the mountains on the coast for three months as the roads were totally washed out and there were numerous landslides. Their Indian caretaker, however, was able to save most everything from the home and clinic.

The river held other perils. Dr. Larry once reported the following near-fatal experience:

"I had a very narrow escape from one of the most danger-ous whirlpools in the great headwaters of the Amazon River. Someone must have been praying that overcast day for the missionaries, when our boat was pulled into those swirling muddy dark waters.

"With only an empty gas tank and strength from the Lord, I was able to stay afloat until a boat was able to drag me from the clutches of those cold waters. I was pulled under numerous times and battered by logs and debris. It was [truly] a miracle because in that lonely stretch of river, a week may pass without a boat coming by. But in that precise moment a boat arrived and, realizing the dangers, three Indians risked their lives to pull this missionary to safety."

Despite the dangers, God blessed Dr. Larry's mission outreach:

"It is fun to watch an emerging Indian church. We are up to our ears just trying to keep up with all that is happening. Our people are accepting the challenge and responsibility of an indigenous church.

"We have many needs and prayer requests. Distances and communications between churches are very difficult. Some of our churches are ten days apart...Some of the churches have planted gardens of which total profits go to the local church. Many of them want to buy metal sheeting for their buildings. Lighting is another difficult problem, and they are in need of pressure lamps."

In 1973 Dr. Larry rejoiced to write the following:

"What a thrill it was to have young men from various parts of the tribe come for the short Bible course in January and February...Some come from as far as three days by foot over rough terrain. These fellows are sincere when they want to learn more about the Bible. We had a wonderful time during the course with many finding spiritual help.

"The Lord is blessing the work, and we are thrilled to be a part of it. There are two new churches under construction now and should be completed within the near future. The prospects for the Aguaruna work are extremely bright, and we are trusting God for great victories.

"The clinic work knows no end. There are always those to adjust, treat medically, and teeth to extract. The Lord has given strength and wisdom in many very difficult cases. Our new Thompson Terminal Point Adjusting Table (provided by the C.C.A.) is getting a lot of use. The Indians have accepted adjustments as part of life now, and they enjoy it very much. The greatest element of surprise though is having the table lift you to a standing position and lay you down by itself. I wish you could see some of their faces and hear the giggles as someone is lowered or raised on that hydraulic table. It is a lot of fun working with a semi-civilized people. They are so unspoiled by things that sharing with them is a joy." (Garman, April 1973)

Dangers and Creativity in Ministry

One aspect of the mission life of Dr. Larry Garman which few missionaries, and probably no other chiropractor, has had any experience is the collecting poisonous snakes for anti-venom.

"We have been sending out a lot of poisonous snakes to make anti-venom. I really enjoy working with them as it is very interesting and also provides the Indians with a little income. They bring them to us, and we send them to the laboratory where they are bought according to their size. It also provides us with free anti-venom. We have had several snakebites, and some of them extremely serious." (Garman, February 1974)

Snakebites were not the only serious health threat. In early 1983, Dr. Larry almost died of typhoid fever and hepatitis. The rainy season caused the roads to be so bad, help could not get to him. When a doctor finally did arrive and wanted to evacuate him to the U.S., that, too, was impossible. They tried to bring in an army helicopter, but even it could not get to them. Finally, prayers alone brought him full recovery. It was against all odds...BUT GOD.

But there were also good times that the family will never forget, for example, the various Christmases on the Marona River.

"Who could forget that first Christmas cantata presented in the jungles? Indians came from four villages to eat several washtubs full of popcorn and experience anew the birth of Christ. That first cantata consisted of a few songs in both the Aguaruna and Spanish languages.

"Addie wanted some...material to make the choir [look] uniform...most [of the members] would be barefooted, some with the typical Indian cloth, a few shirts and homemade dresses, some with holes and patches. Our problem was isolation, and therefore [there was] nothing to purchase. So I recommended blue colored toilet paper, draping strips over the shoulders of each member of her choir.

"Another Christmas when Rusty, Greg, and Candy flew home from school, we put up a huge sign in the front yard welcoming them home. We brought large skyrockets to shoot off as the pontoon plane approached. We gave the matches to a young Indian man to light the skyrockets as the plane circled overhead. He got excited and misguided the rockets and nearly shot the plane out of the sky. The pilot, after landing, was not very amused by his mistake.

"Another year, we had no wrapping paper, so the children made their own with newspaper and crayons."

The Garmans retired from their mission in 2002. Without a doubt, they are a perfect example of servants, used of God in a most difficult location. They have seen the beauty and not just the problems, provided health service in every way possible, preached the Gospel to a people who had no other way to hear the Word, won thousands to the Lord, established hundreds of churches and loved their 37 years of ministry. Furthermore, they raised a beautiful family, all of whom love and serve the Lord and are well adjusted in every way. The Christian Chiropractors Association is proud to have been able to have had just a small part in this most outstanding ministry.

Malaysia, Vietnam, Ecuador, Canada, and Columbia
Dr. and Mrs. John Hall

John Hall was yet another person inspired by Dr. Robert N. Thompson to be a missionary chiropractor. John graduated from Canadian Memorial Chiropractic College in Toronto in 1960. John and Penny

Dr. John and Penny Hall, daughter Ilana

Hall began their service in June 1966 with the Christian & Missionary Alliance in Malaysia. They taught in a school for missionary children, and Dr. John had many opportunities to use his professional skill, particularly aiding other missionaries.

Ministry in Malaysia

"As I write this letter, I am sitting in the Overseas Missionary Fellowship Home in Kuala Lumpur. My wife and I are just returning from a week's stay in Singapore with a teacher from the OMF Bible College...whom I had treated previously for an acute back... We had a very enjoyable time in Singapore, which is a very beautiful and progressive city and rapidly becoming more and more westernized.

"From Singapore we went to the beach at Port Dickson on the West Coast of Malaysia on the Straits of Malacca. A young medical missionary with the Baptist work in Indonesia...requested treatment of an acute torticollis he had obtained while sleeping in an awkward position in a plane, I was glad to be of help with a few adjustments.

"During school...I treated several students and visiting missionaries for various conditions. One teenager, who has been suffering from grand mal epilepsy for about two years, responded quite well to treatment and improved considerably. Because of our heavy teaching schedule, which my wife and I

*have found very interesting, challenging, and thrilling, I have not
had time nor opportunity for an outreach to the local people.
Our lack of space is another reason for this; however, this
coming semester we are moving from our one room into a two
room arrangement, with two closed-in porches, which may help."*
(Hall, Jan. 1967)

Ministry in Vietnam

In Spring 1967, Dr. John and Penny traveled to Vietnam for a
field conference, and a new work was begun:

*"We heard wonderful reports from the various stations and
special ministries, how God was reaching souls for His kingdom.
The war has opened many opportunities to reach the lost, and
hearts are more receptive than they have ever been in the past.*

*"At the conference Penny and I were appointed to field
work in Vietnam, and so we are presently moving to the old
school location in Dalat for language study. Please remember
us in your prayers that we may readily grasp Vietnamese during
this year of study. We are not sure of where God will lead us
from here, however. I am very interested in the leprosarium at
Ban Mi Thout, and it may be God's plan to take us into this work
once we have the language. We praise Him for His leading thus
far and His keeping power as he supplies all our needs according to His riches in glory by Christ Jesus."*

Wartime Evacuations

Dr. John did get involved in the leprosy work in Ban Mi Thout,
Vietnam, and Penny became involved in translation of the Jerai tribal
language. Their work, however, was interrupted in January 1968 by
the Tet offensive. The North Vietnamese staged an all out attack on
the South, the Americans, and the missionaries. Six missionaries were
killed, and several others were taken captive. The Halls were evacuated from Dalat, to Camh Run Bay and then to Bangkok, Thailand.

The airplane which picked them up was not even able to actually
stop: instead, as it moved slowly down the runway, Dr. John lifted a
very pregnant Penny and himself into the moving plane which then
took off as fast as it could. Penny almost lost what was to be their only
child, daughter Ilana.

A few weeks later Dr. Glenn Stillwagon, Dr. Harry Kalsbeek, and
I contacted the Halls in Thailand on our way into Vietnam, but we
never got to visit with them there. *(More about this in the chapter,
"World Tour.")*

That August, Dr. John returned to Vietnam. Penny and Ilana, who was born in Thailand, joined him in September, and they settled in Saigon.

"We were able to recover almost all of our belongings from Dalat, so I have my adjusting table here in Saigon. Except for a few small items, which were missing, everything was in good condition. I...shipped them to Saigon by truck. There are no language students in Dalat now, just one senior missionary couple. The national missionaries are all on their stations and the language students are distributed throughout various cities in the country.

"My mission has asked if I would be interested in the leprosy work in Pleiku-Ban Mi Tuot area, and if so I will need to take some special courses related to treating leprosy. I am very anxious to talk with Dr. Bob Thompson about this when he is here next week."

Dr. Thompson did visit the Halls in Vietnam in December 1968, and once again Dr. John was inspired.

"We had an especially happy pre-Christmas week because Dr. Bob Thompson was in town, and we had a few pleasant hours together with him. He was instrumental in my salvation back in 1961, and as a result, had a part in my meeting Penny, and so we were more than pleased to see him and to show off our little daughter, Ilana. I was glad for the opportunity to chat with him about my future work with leprosy even though our time was limited because of the heavy schedule of the World Anti-Communist League Conference which he was attending."

During his time in Saigon, Dr. John had a fruitful evangelism ministry among the South Vietnamese military as well as in a large military hospital. He stated, "thousands have turned to Christ!" However, Dr. John was again evacuated in 1972, this time from his mission station in Pleiku.

"First of all I should say that we are all well and safe. We have been waiting and watching...for the enemy to make his move. At Tet time, in February, our New York headquarters ordered all of us out of the highlands, because they did not want another occurrence like...in 1968 when six of our colleagues were killed by the North Vietnamese soldiers. We were here in Saigon for one week and then two weeks in Nhatrang before returning to Pleiku to continue to wait for what the military knew was coming, but had no idea when it would come.

"Penny and Ilana were the first to leave Pleiku for Saigon, and a few days later the chief of civilian operations and the military advised us to leave. In fact most of the population of Pleiku has moved to other more secure cities. If Kontum falls,

Pleiku will get hit hard. So far Pleiku has escaped. If Pleiku is attacked, the military feel sure they can hold it; however, there will be a great deal of destruction.

"We have brought a few of our valuable items with us and a Vietnamese Christian drove my car from Pleiku to Saigon...My language teacher came in the car, so I can continue to study while we wait here in Saigon. We have no idea when we will be able to return.

"Continue to pray for us, for the leaders, and for this nation. We believe God is going to do much more here than He has done already. All over this country God is moving with revival blessings and also the salvation of many souls. Yesterday I went to a refugee camp where Steing tribal people from An Loc are located, and seven received Christ as their Savior. Last Sunday 23 believed.

"We heard that the Jerai people in Pleiku who are still there are meeting morning, noon, and night to pray. At prayer meeting tonight we heard a tremendous testimony of the power of God by a Vietnamese major who has become administrative director of the 3000-bed military hospital here in Saigon where I used to go for our special meetings every Sunday evening last term.

"Everywhere I go, people come to me for chiropractic adjustments–missionaries, nationals, American military and civilians. We thank the Lord for your prayers. The Lord is with us." (Hall, June 1972)

Dr. John continued his ministry in Vietnam, and at the height of the war in 1973 wrote the following:

"We rejoice in the way the Lord is able to transform individual lives. During this past year as we have gone out witnessing with the young people from the Pleiku church, over 1,000 people in the villages and refugee camps have responded to the Gospel. On Christmas day seventy-three followed the Lord in baptism. Many of these new believers attended one of these short-term Bible school sessions held on our mission property. It was a real thrill to have a part in teaching at these sessions.

"As we praise the Lord for these things, let us continue to pray that the fighting that is still going on in some areas will end so that the thousands of refugees can return to their former areas in safety. Pray that they will continue to follow Christ, and that it will be safe for some of us to go and teach and help them form new churches. We have not been able to get to a number of our clinics because of poor security. We believe that prayer can change this situation.

"Penny would appreciate your prayers as she begins working on an overview of the Old Testament, beginning with the first eleven chapters of Genesis.

"In my last letter I mentioned that Penny's parents were coming for Christmas. We had a wonderful time together here in Pleiku and also during our month's vacation. What kind of vacation does a missionary chiropractor have, any way? It was probably not the kind of vacation that you would like to have, because this chiropractor gave adjustments almost every day.

"When I arrived in Singapore, a former acquaintance requested professional help. He is dean of the Singapore Bible College and had suffered a back injury about six months ago. An orthopedic specialist ordered traction and six weeks in bed. Finally, after several months he was told that there was nothing else to do but wait. Wait he did, in constant pain and unable to drive his own car. What else could I do when I heard his story? After the first spinal adjustment the severe pain was gone. Needless to say, I treated him all the time I was in Singapore, and then he flew to Penang for more adjustments during the ten days we were there.

"After his first adjustment, he asked if I would examine a Christian writer. And so I also treated this Chinese author, a relative of Watchman Nee. Before long a former patient who had flown from Singapore to Saigon for treatments during our last term came for treatments too...

"When I arrived back in Saigon after our vacation, I learned that the director of Wycliffe Bible Translators for Vietnam, Dick Watson, had asked our business agent to buy a ticket for me to Dalat so that I could ...help one of their linguists who had been completely bed-ridden with sciatica for two weeks. I thank the Lord for the way He enables...in all of these situations. How grateful I am that we are co-laborers in the Lord's service. May the Lord richly bless each one of you according to His riches in Glory." (Hall, March 1973)

Two years later, the Halls were once again evacuated.

"As you have heard in the news, Vietnam is going through very dark days. We are safe in Thailand. On Wednesday, March 12, I left Pleiku for Saigon. Penny had gone the day before. We were in Saigon until March 21. It was decided that we should come here to Bangkok for a few days, and then Penny would be allowed to go to Penang to take Ilana out of the mission boarding school so that we could leave for furlough early. While Penny is in Penang, I will [travel] to Udorn to treat

one of our missionaries there, and another from Vientiane, Loas, will come across the border to Udorn, which is not very far, and take some treatments also.

"I am leaving Bangkok for Udorn on Friday, March 28, and will return to Bangkok on Friday, April 3. These are hectic days, but God is faithful and full of mercy. We praise His Name. I will be looking forward to sharing with you all that He has done." (Hall, March 1975)

Ministry to Vietnamese Refugees in Canada

Vietnam fell to the Communists on April 25, 1975. Unable to return, the Halls came home to Canada, and Dr. John pastored a church while he and Penny began a ministry to Vietnam refugees in the Montreal area.

"As we continued to meet more refugee families, increasingly we came up against the problem of how to help these people in a material way with the necessities of life to carry on in this new country. Unlike those who have been sponsored by groups or individuals in the United States, the refugees coming to Canada are government sponsored. Although quite adequately cared for with food and temporary shelter, they must go it alone in finding work, housing, furniture, and all the other basic needs to set up a new home.

"We sent out a plea for help to the churches in our district. We made known the need for clothing, furniture, linens, dishes, etc. As these things were brought by truck, the tangible demonstration of Christian love and concern has done much to help these people in a practical way and also win their friendship and confidence.

"Among our earliest contacts were a doctor and his wife, a lawyer. When they located an apartment, we gave them some furniture and helped them move. Later... as Penny and I visited in their apartment, both of them accepted the Lord as their Savior. Several pharmacists, a high school teacher, a professor from Saigon University, a politician and his wife, and an engineer and his wife, are some of those who quickly responded to the Gospel. One day I had the thrill of leading an architect, his wife, and five teenage children to a saving knowledge of Christ.

"Penny and I are anticipating further service overseas. We covet your prayers as we seek the Lord's guidance for our future ministry. Thank you again for all that you mean to us and have done for us. And for standing with us as we seek His will." (Hall, January 1976)

Ministry in Ecuador

In 1977 the Lord called the Halls to Ecuador. Before they could go, however, they had to spend a year in language study in Costa Rica. Dr. John reported that the intensity of the one-year course did not leave much time for anything but study. However, he did continue his chiropractic ministry:

"I have a number of the language school students as patients. A few of them have brought Costa Rican friends for adjustments also."

In 1979 the Halls were stationed on the upper and lower Napo River in eastern Ecuador. They evangelized, taught the Bible, and planted new churches among the Quichua Indians. John actively used his chiropractic training in his ministry, adjusting hundreds of Spanish-speaking Ecuadorians, Quichuan Indians and missionaries during his years of service. His only frustration was that there was little opportunity to follow-up on the care he gave.

"The challenge here is tremendous, both spiritually and physically. At this writing I am on a week-long trip aboard a forty-foot dugout canoe on the Napo River, a major tributary of the Amazon. The first day we traveled on the fastest moving section of the river, through rapids and small whirlpools. At times torrential downpours continued for hours and transformed the river into an angry, surging giant. At this point...the Napo is about a kilometer wide.

"I am with an evangelistic team of Quichua workers and a group of three musicians visiting a new area...farther down the Napo than our missionaries have ever gone...We were well received, and they want us to return. It took us about fifteen hours of river travel to get here. The jungle, or 'Oriente,' as it is called, is vast, and the people live in small isolated groups of about 30 to 50 families all along the river, which stretches for miles and miles. Pray that I will have wisdom to know how to effectively reach them.

"This work is thrilling on the one hand, but overwhelming ...on the other. We need great physical strength and spiritual insight. I thank the Lord for good health and renewed strength. Pray for Penny. She has been having intestinal problems. Many of the natives come to me with physical problems. For these I need unusual wisdom. During the last month I have been treating an 11-year-old girl who was kicked by a horse about three years ago. She has been improving, so we have won the confidence of her parents. Pray for us as we counsel and work with these people." (Hall, May 1980)

Later Dr. John wrote: "The work here has been discouraging. The churches are cold and the people are backsliding continually. Much to our dismay, during the past three years we have seen no reversal in this trend. Materialism seems to have firm grip on the people for one thing, and secondly we really wonder if they ever realized the true meaning of repentance in the beginning of their Christian life. We thank the Lord for the few who are faithful and with whom we have been able to work in discipleship and training. We go home on furlough deeply concerned for these people." (Hall 1982)

On their second term of service in Ecuador, the Halls moved down river to the town of Lago Agrio, a city of 20,000 people where a mission station had been developed but was in need of additional workers. Dr. John had visited this city during his previous tour of duty and even before they moved in he had patients waiting for him.

The C.C.A. bought two 55-horse-power motors for boats for the missionaries to travel up and down the river.

"Thank you so much to all of the members who helped us obtain the two motors for our boats which are so essential for our work up and down the Napo River. I have been teaching homiletics and church history at our Bible Institute in Tena this past week, and I will be teaching all of this coming week. As usual, wherever I go there are people who want adjustments. These have been busy days teaching in Lago Agrio and in Tena, and treating complicated cases. Now I am having trouble with my own back. Life here is very strenuous, and there is much to do. Please pray for me!" (Hall, Summer 1984)

Dr. John also reported that, because Lago Agrio was in the middle of the eastern Ecuadorian oil field, he had opportunity to serve many of the workers there.

"I treated a number of nationals who work for the Texaco Petroleum Company. There are about 800 men at their Lago Agrio base camp. My first patient from the base was one of the administrators who responded unusually fast. As a result, I enjoyed a good relationship with the base medical doctor, who referred patients to me right up to the day before I left for furlough. The appreciation of the Texaco Company was shown to us in many different ways, which made life and work in Lago Agrio so much easier.

"I think that a good indication of the acceptance of chiropractic in our area was the constant inquiry before I left for furlough, 'Is anyone coming to replace you?' Unfortunately there was not!"

During his time in Ecuador, Dr. John also served on the Executive Committee of the Christian and Missionary Alliance Mission of Ecuador and on the board of the Alliance Academy in Quito. In summing up their ministries, Dr. John Hall wrote:

"We have lived as missionaries in four Third World countries over the past 21 years. During this time we have studied three foreign languages. In 1966, I sensed God calling me to Southeast Asia. I left my chiropractic practice in Canada to teach, along with my wife, in a school for missionaries' children in Malaysia. The following year we were engaged in Vietnamese language study, and for the next two years we did evangelistic work in the large Vietnamese military hospital in Saigon, Vietnam.

"Our second term took us to the Central Highlands of Viet Nam where we studied Jerai, a tribal language. While serving as director of rehabilitation in the Pleiku leprosy clinic, I carried on a preaching and teaching ministry in the Jerai and Vietnamese churches of that area until all of the missionaries were forced to leave the country in 1975.

"After completing Spanish language study in Costa Rica in 1979, our ministry during our third term was primarily among the lowland Quichua Indians along the Napo River in the Amazonian jungles of Equador.

"In 1983, at the beginning of our fourth term we moved to the town of Lago Agrio, which is located deeper in the jungle in the remote northeastern region of Equador. There we established a church and dedicated a new building, which will seat about 300 people. Our ministry included evangelism, church planting, discipleship, teaching, and health care.

"...it appears that we will not be able to return to Lago Agrio when our furlough ends in 1988. Penny, my wife, is suffering from innumerable allergies, the most critical being an allergy to dust, which cannot be avoided in that area because of the gravel roads. Thank you so much for your love, your prayers and for your faithful support in every way." (Hall, 1987)

The Halls left Ecuador in 1987 because of Penny's health. Dr. John went back into private practice in Ontario, Canada. Penny, who had a degree in cultural anthropology from Carleton University, went to the University of Edinburgh, Scotland, and received her Ph.D. in Hebrew. Penny had always been a talented translator and her pursuit of the Ph.D. was another step in this field.

Ministry in Colombian Prisons

In 1991, Dr. John made a short term mission trip to Columbia to give chiropractic care and preach the Gospel in the prisons in Bogota. Dr. Hall filed the following report upon his return from Bogota:

"On November 23, 1991, Dr. Eric Jackson and I went to Bogota, Columbia for two weeks to provide chiropractic care for prisoners in three of the city's major prisons. Before going to a place like Bogota, we had to admit we were anxious about a number of things.

"We really did not know what to expect, but we did know that we went trusting in God. We also knew that the Bible says in Hebrews Chapter 13: 'Remember those in prison as if you were their fellow prisoner, and those who are mistreated as if you yourselves are suffering.' We want to assure you that we were very much aware of the prayers of God's people as we encountered the powers of darkness behind those prison bars in Bogota.

"This was the first time either one of us had given chiro-practic adjustments behind bars, and as far as we know it was the first time that chiropractors had been in the prisons there. The CCA received a request from Action International Ministries for a team of chiropractors to go in November. Ernie Whiteside, a missionary with Action, set up our schedule.

"Our primary objective was to supplement the work of Prison Fellowship by sharing the love of Christ in a practical way, and assist them in gaining a better hearing for the Gospel. Each morning we prayed together with Ernie and then set out for the day to 'please God, not men' (I Thess. 2:4), and God blessed our work. Altogether we treated about 600 people including missionaries from several mission agencies.

"In some cases we saw amazing results. One missionary, who Eric treated, had such a severe shoulder problem she was headed for surgery. After the first adjustment, there was remark-able improvement. Even Eric was surprised. By the time we left, her shoulder problem was cleared up.

"In the prisons security checked everything: our person, our cameras, our tables including the padding, even our lunches. There was such a positive reception and good response every-where that we had to keep on reminding ourselves that these people were prisoners. On the third day at the women's prison, after sharing about his life and faith, Eric had the great joy of leading his interpreter to the Lord. She was a prisoner who had volunteered to help.

"We treated not only the prisoners, but the guards, the administrative staff, the chief of medical department, other doctors, as well as the director of the prison and his assistant. Later that week Ernie was asked if we could go to the Ministry of Justice because they had heard how we had created such a spirit of togetherness and sense of unity, the justice minister wanted us to come and do the same thing for his staff.

"... Our work began with a mountaintop experience in the women's prison, but the maximum-security prison was another story. There we felt the oppression of the enemy. We became discouraged. The prisoners at first were more difficult to relate to. We had never seen so many scars from knife wounds and bullet holes. But then God turned our attitudes around, and it proved to be a profitable time there, too, as we had opportunity to show God's love to the young man who had assassinated the justice minister five years before.

"In the third prison, we were adjusting in the Prison Fellowship physiotherapy room, which was right next to the chapel. What a thrill to work to the sound of Christian choruses, as some 70-90 prisoners gathered to sing praises to God under the direction of the Prison Fellowship chaplain.

"This trip was a great experience. God kept us well, erased all of our anxieties, and gave us the strength for each day. It was amazing to see how the love of God broke down all barriers. Perhaps you see barriers against going on a short-term mission. God can remove them in a way that will amaze you, and allow His love to flow through you in a way that will change your life forever." (Hall, 1991)

New Guinea
Dr. and Mrs. Brinsley Lane

It was 1942; General Douglas MacArthur was white with rage at the animated conversation in the other room. Who was this Australian officer, an unknown rascal who wished to give him advice?

"Tell MacArthur he is making a mistake if he lands at that point on the coast of New Guinea. I'll advise him and direct him to the best landing beach on New Guinea."

Who does he think he is? Didn't this stranger know that he was to be addressed as "Your Excellency" or "The General" or "General MacArthur?" Never as just "MacArthur!" Didn't he know that he was talking about the great American general, probably one of the greatest generals of all time? He talked to God! He talked to Presidents! He talked to other generals, to colonels and Senators, majors and, on special rare occasions, even to some mere captains. Others didn't tell him he was making a mistake; he didn't make mistakes!

Perhaps he was also white with rage because there was an apparent gross breach of security. Only a handful of high-ranking officers knew his first counterattack plan against the Japanese. Yet, here was a total stranger able to identify his intended landing site. If this could be done so easily, could not Japanese intelligence also be able to penetrate this security, prepare a strong defense, and ruin his invasion plans?

This was war! He would have the man interrogated to find the breach of security. He gave orders to have the man brought before him.

"General MacArthur, my name is Lane. Before the war, I had a plantation farm along the coast of New Guinea at this point." He said, as he pointed to a spot on the coast of New Guinea on the large map on the wall.

"On my farm was a short, but ideal beach for an invasion landing that hardly anyone knows about. Since it is on my farm, I can lead you right to it. Just before we had to leave, there was a terrible typhoon which totally... changed the beach...here," he said, again pointing to a place on the map. *"This map doesn't show that area of change."*

"And oh, you needn't worry about any breach of security. I am the only officer in the Australian army who has spent any amount of time in New Guinea in the last few years, and from the casual interrogation that was given about New Guinea, I just deduced that this was a probability."

General MacArthur listened. Somehow, this young Lane fellow sounded convincing and straightforward. He liked him. And if he was right…a bad landing beach would lead to catastrophe.

After a complete security check, the general did take Lane's advice, and the troops did land on Lane's farm, which proved a total success, with very few casualties. Out of curiosity, MacArthur did survey his original invasion site. It was even worse than Lane had described. It would have indeed been a debacle. Officer Lane had played a small–but important–part in returning peace to New Guinea. Years later, Officer Lane's cousin Brinsley Lane continued the family's connection with New Guinea.

After college, Brinsley Lane became a teacher, got married, and started raising a family. Because of some health problems, Brin decided to visit a chiropractor in Australia. The results were fantastic, and he became enamored with the concept of natural health through chiropractic.

He continued to read his Bible and began to pray about a career change while examining the science and logic of chiropractic. He came to believe God was confirming him to this change. He sold his house, packed up his family, and moved to Canada. When Dr. Brin Lane graduated from Canadian Memorial Chiropractic College in Toronto, Ontario, he and his wife Meg, and their three children dedicated their lives to missionary service for their Lord.

Dr. Brin & Meg Lane
Mark, Julie & Brinsly, Jr.

While in chiropractic college, he met a member of the Christian Chiropractors Association who had spent some time as a missionary chiropractor in New Guinea with the Wycliffe Bible Translators. Remembering the story about his cousin and General MacArthur, he felt a special relationship to this land.

Arrival in New Guinea

After a short trip to their native Australia, the Lanes traveled to Papau, New Guinea, and set up a chiropractic mission station with the Wycliff Bible Translators at Ukarumpa. Dr. Brin wrote the following after their arrival in New Guinea:

"We flew up from Sydney, to Lae, New Guinea, on January 26, 1973. On Tuesday, January 30, we came up to Ukarumpa by Land Rover. The country is very beautiful, but I can't say the same for the roads. Driving in New Guinea is hazardous as, outside of the towns, roads, if they exist at all, are mostly not paved. There are numerous trucks, and although road rules exist, they are often not observed. There are many New Guinean pedestrians and one has to drive very carefully. A warning is given to Europeans especially NOT to stop in the event of hitting a pedestrian as the [locals] would attack and probably kill the occupants of the vehicle, not to mention occupants of any other vehicle in the vicinity. The old custom of 'payback' is still very much alive.

"We received a warm welcome on our arrival in Ukarumpa and are settled in a house belonging to a translator family absent on sick leave. Our three children have settled into school: Julie and Brinsley in the high school here on base, and Mark in grade 5 at the elementary school at Aiytra, which is about 2 miles away near the airstrip. All elementary school children this year travel in a fine new SIL bus. (Summer Institute of Linguistics, as Wycliffe Bible Translators is called on the field)

"Meg and I started work on Monday, February 5. Meg is involved with minding the one-year-olds in the nursery each day from 8:15 till 11:30. All the wives on base are expected to do some sort of voluntary work. I have been given the use of the emergency maternity room at the medical clinic here. It is rather cluttered and in an emergency has to be vacated, but it is possible to operate, and I have gone ahead.

"The only equipment I have at present is a wooden bench table, which I had made at the joinery shop here. So far I have seen some 50 - 60 patients in each of the three weeks of operation. No charge is made for either medical or my chiropractic services beyond a token clinic fee of 50 cents, which goes into clinic funds. I expect the numbers to increase as more people return to base from their tribal locations, from furlough, and from summer school in Australia. Also I understand there should be more patients from outside SIL as the word of our arrival spreads.

"I may be able to make a weekly overnight visit to Lae, by air, to catch missionaries in, around, or passing through there. I am making my second such visit on Monday and am still investigating the pros and cons of this. We now hope to remain here at Ukarumpa and have our headquarters here. In order to do this, it will be necessary to join SIL as short-term assistants. This was our intention originally, about twelve months back, so we have been brought the full circle.

"The main thing to be thrashed out yet with the directors of SIL is the amount of freedom I can have during the time I am not seeing patients here on base. SIL normally requires its members to make up some time in other SIL activity if not fully occupied in the primary calling. At this moment we are negotiating.

"… I'd like…to begin a postural survey and preliminary investigation programme within the two schools here. For this I need some equipment for measurement.

"Relationships here between the M.D. and myself are cordial, and I see no reason why they should not remain so. The permanent M.D. is…on leave in Canada till about July. The present man, Dr. Myrholme is also a Canadian. He arrived only last week and expects to be here till June.

"Ukarumpa is a beautiful setting, in a valley some 5000 feet altitude, in the Eastern Highlands. It has 250 houses within its facilities, a print shop, an auto shop, joinery, a sawmill, etc.; it is unique. At times it is difficult to believe it is an expanded missionary base until you look out across the hills and see native villages in the distance, or go to church on Sunday and see the whole town there!

"We still see a tremendous need for chiropractic here. As far as I know, there is only one other chiropractor…in the whole of Papua, New Guinea, and she may not stay beyond this year. There are many missionaries. Some modern facilities make their work more efficient, but the stresses attending their work are manifold. Many of them lose much time through illness. I do not think we can replace medical services on the mission field nor am I sure there can always be fully cooperative effort because of the many opposing facets of our respective philosophies, but I am certain that a useful co-existence is not only possible but absolutely essential.

"I praise the Lord for (1) the wonderful sense of being in the right place at the right time (I, being in the way, the Lord led me); (2) A safe arrival and a warm welcome; (3) Being a part of a

team involved in the most worthwhile of all tasks, that of putting the Scriptures into the hands of people in their own languages; (4) The awareness of the prayers of many SIL members who have been praying for our arrival for many months; (5) Excellent results already from clinic practice; and (6) Warm personal relationship established with three young men from the Wiru tribe who come to meals once a week with our family. Praise the Lord!" (Lane, March 1973)

Return to Australia

Dr. Lane's chiropractic ministry in Ukarumpa was much appreciated by the mission and many others in the area. He reported that he treated over 500 different patients, including 350 from the Summer Institutes of Linguistics, 100 local New Guineans, and 50 other tribal people. The medical clinic on the base was remodeled to include space for a chiropractic clinic.

Unfortunately the Lanes did not have adequate support from a sponsoring church or other organization, and the Christian Chiropractors Association, not being a mission sending organization, was not able to totally support them. Therefore, they had to curtail their ministry due to lack of adequate financial support. The Wycliffe missionaries were very supportive, giving them all the help they could. At the time of their leaving, many of his patients asked, "What are we going to do now?"

The Lanes moved to Western Australia where Dr. Lane established a private practice. Probably as a result of the stress of mission life, he suffered a heart attack in May 1978 and died at a relatively young age shortly after his return to Western Australia. The Lane children were only 19, 17, and 15 at the time. Meg Lane went back to teaching school after Dr. Brin's passing.

While Officer Lane had played a part in returning military peace to New Guinea, Dr. Brinsley Lane had played no small part in bringing physical health and spiritual peace to many in this same country.

Canada
Dr. and Mrs. Donald Cox

In the cold northeast portion of Quebec, Canada, Dr. Donald E. Cox served as pastor of an evangelical outreach together with his wife, Beth, three sons, and one daughter. The area was one of the most needy areas in all of North America, so Dr. Cox partially supported his ministry as a doctor of chiropractic.

"[Our practice] does not really support our ministry financially. The four churches that have commended us to this pioneer work in Quebec encouraged us to maintain our professional status, but we depend on their help as well. They and other assemblies and individuals are the means through which the Lord provides.

"Our ministry here is a pioneer work. No testimony of any kind has existed in the past. Through visitation and witnessing, souls have come to the Lord and have been brought into the local church fellowship, and now we have the added responsibility of pastoring the flock.

"Our goal is the formation of a local assembly, built on the simplicity of the New Testament church principles, under the guidance of local elders and pastors. This means that within a certain time we will be leaving in order to plant elsewhere. I am sure you realize the prayer that is needed to confront the many obstacles from without and within.

"We thank God that it is His church and that He sees to it that the testimony grows and remains. It is exciting to see changes in the personalities of the new believers who become stable, some of them becoming true shepherds. We thank the Lord for those of the C.C.A. who have been praying for us and who have been able to give financially from time to time."

This area was all French speaking and of course the Coxes spoke French. Winters were extremely severe; therefore, most of their ministry had to be done in the summer months. During these warmer months, the Coxes used summer camps as an outreach to young people, many of whom had no other place to hear the Gospel of Jesus Christ.

Their first years of ministry were in Drummondville, Quebec, but in 1973 they moved out on the Gaspe Peninsula, to the village of St. Anne des Monts. Dr. Cox wrote about life there:

"We have found a house to buy here which can be used for Bible study groups and is also well laid out to begin a new

practice. There is no evangelical testimony and no chiropractor. We cherish the prayers of the Lord's people in this new pioneer area. A few have been saved during past visits, and there are hundreds of contacts.

"Presently we treat 30 to 40 patients per week by working on Tuesday and Thursday afternoons and evenings. This is in spite of the fact that there is 80% unemployment in this area. The balance of the week, I spend doing visitation and evangelism and pastoral work.

"Our family...keeps my wife and I both busy also. There are no Christian young people in this area as yet and so our young ones miss that fellowship. We thank God for the children He has given us. They have adapted well to the environment here and are doing very well in the French Catholic schools."

As the children grew older, there was a need for better schools and facilities for them. So in 1981, the Coxes moved south to Three Rivers, Quebec. Their two oldest, David and Carolyn, were in university. David went on to become a chiropractor, graduating from Canadian Memorial Chiropractic College in 1986.

Their two youngest sons, Timmy and Kevin had Crohn's disease, a severe intestinal condition that had no cure but could be helped with careful diet. They both had several inches of their intestines removed as teenagers. This brought some much-appreciated relief.

On April 21, 1993, in a blinding snowstorm, the Cox's only daughter, Carolyn, was killed in a tragic automobile/truck accident. She was only 29 years old and was teaching school at the time.

Dr. Don and Beth continued their church mission outreach, and developed an itinerate ministry, returning periodically to the areas in Quebec where they had served in past years. Theirs was a difficult ministry in a cold and remote area. It was against all odds ...but God.

Dr. Don & Beth Cox
Timothy, Carolyn, David & Kevin

Monaco
Dr. and Mrs. David Cox

Dr. David Cox *(no relation to Dr. Donald Cox profiled in the previous chapter)* graduated from Cleveland Chiropractic College in Los Angeles in 1965 and started practice in Long Beach. However, he knew God wanted him on the mission field. His wife, Phyllis, had been a missionary before they were married, and she, too, knew that was where God wanted them to be. They had three children, Mayda, who would later follow her father's footsteps in becoming a chiropractor, and two sons, Tim and Philip.

In September 1970 Dr. Cox sold his California home and practice and flew to New York with his family. From there they sailed for Europe.

> *"The Lord is leading us to Monaco, 370 acres and 23,500 people on the south coast of France with no Gospel witness. As yet we have no address for we go as Abraham went, trusting only in God to open and close the doors which affect us. Trans World Radio broadcasts the Christian message from Monte Carlo, Cyprus, and Guam into Europe, Africa, the Middle East, the South Pacific, and Asia; and we are assured the Lord has a big job for us to do in conjunction with that ministry." (Cox, 1970)*

The Coxes went to Europe largely in a bi-professional capacity. Dr. Dave was appointed to the technical department at the headquarters of Trans World Radio in Monaco. This gave him the opportunity for service as well as the freedom to continue his chiropractic ministry. His ministry spread beyond TWR as he traveled to group meetings, conventions, and seminars throughout much of Europe to give chiropractic care to missionaries attending these meetings.

Dr. David and Phyllis Cox
Tim, Mayda & Philip

Behind the Iron Curtain

In addition, as a Gideon, Dr. Dave placed Bibles in some of the large resort hotels and Roman Catholic schools in Monaco. He also delivered Bibles into Eastern Europe at a time when that was a very dangerous project. In October 1971 Dr. Dave described one of those trips:

"[In] July, while Phyllis helped the children with their French lessons at home, I accompanied a missionary couple by auto into Turkey, Iran, Afghanistan, and two Iron Curtain countries. [To save the identities of those he visited, he did not give us the names of the countries he visited at that time, but now we can reveal that they were Yugoslavia and Bulgaria. Ed.] *We had the privilege of delivering two boxes of Bibles and tracts behind the Iron Curtain and seeing the Lord work in a mighty way getting this precious seed across the border.*

"It wasn't until five days later that we really knew what the Lord had done for us. A man had stopped to help us because of trouble with our car and asked us how we had made out going through the border, since we were pulling a small camp trailer. When we told him they only looked in our trunk and waved us on, he just couldn't believe it. He had come through the day after we did, and it took him four hours to get through. He said it was not just himself, but everyone there was searched piece by piece. You can imagine how we praised the Lord. If we had been caught, the car would have been impounded, and we would have been put in jail. The wonderful hand of God does protect His children.

"There in one of those Iron Curtain countries, we met an 80-year-old pastor. He greeted us with outstretched arms as we entered the living room of the small apartment on the third floor. Intensive study of the Word of God and many years of extreme persecution have left his eyesight very dim. But in spite of it all, he is in the pulpit faithfully giving out God's Word every Sunday. He told us that he was the only one licensed to preach in that church, and when he stopped, they would close the doors. So he said he had told the Lord he would be faithful till death to feed the flock the Lord had given him. How our hearts did cry out for this pastor and the other dear Christians we met behind the Iron Curtain.

"When we arrived at Istanbul, Turkey, we really knew we were in a different part of the world, and rightly so, for here Europe ends and Asia begins. Living conditions in general were poor. We saw many accidents, and on several occasions, deaths. We do thank the Lord for His safe protection... for we traveled at a very hurried pace in order to keep our schedule.

"In Tehran, Iran, we attended a Bible conference and had a wonderful time of fellowship. This was sponsored by the Bible Society of Tehran, which was established there in 1814. I met and helped Dr. Flora Colby who is also a C.C.A. missionary. Each Thursday and Saturday morning she goes to the Kennedy Rehabilitation Centre for retarded children. There we adjusted many needy and grateful children.

"After a very hot and tiring journey we arrived in Kabul, Afghanistan, our final destination. We saw how the Lord has been blessing the 25 years of untiring service of Dr. and Mrs. Christy Wilson. The government has at last allowed them to finish building their new church after a year's delay. This indeed is an answer to the prayers of many. I was the guest in the home of Col. and Mrs. Richard McTaggart. The Colonel is in charge of defense attaché for the American embassy staff of Afghanistan.

"It was indeed a very special privilege to be used of the Lord in a two fold way, for everywhere we went there were physical and spiritual needs."

In 1972 Phyllis Cox reported from her perspective:

"David had a session with a group from Monaco for a study of the places we visited in the Holy Land and their significance in Biblical prophecy. One of the group suggested that we have a continuing Bible study. Ahead we see undreamed of potential in turning many to Christ. It seems as if the Lord is giving us those who are really hungry and ready for a deeper work of His grace. This assures us of your prayers behind us.

"Five weeks ago we started a ladies' Bible class with four nationalities represented: Dutch, English, Russian and American. It is thrilling to see how the Lord has worked–and is working–in these hearts. They are so earnest in studying the Bible. We also have a children's Bible club on Thursday mornings, which takes the place of Sunday school and is exciting to see the little ones talk enthusiastically of 'having Jesus in my heart'.

"We have found that Christian believers have been very timid about expressing their faith. They have had no Christian fellowship and little Bible teaching. They have grown cold and indifferent. Little by little they are beginning to share their spiritual experiences and faith in the Lord. Many attend church and feel they are Christians, but have had no experience with Christ to make it valid. Only the Holy Spirit can do that. Do pray that all may experience the love of God and receive the necessary power to live Christ's life."

In 1976 the C.C.A. office received a letter from a Campus Crusade for Christ missionary, Ann Pedicord, who had been a patient of Dr. Cox. She described some changes in the Coxes' ministry.

"The other evening we drove to a nearby German town to see Dr. Cox...we were surprised, and I must say delighted, to see a new adjusting table sitting in the middle of the living room. Clark and I just wanted to...thank you and the rest of the Christian Chiropractors for sending this portable table. [Dr. Cox]... is doing a tremendous work everywhere he goes and this table makes adjustments so much easier and better.

"We discovered something else this visit that we thought you would find interesting too. Some other people shared this with us because Dr. Cox was hurrying to another place to help others. Dr. and Mrs. Cox are living almost completely by faith due to some very exciting tasks that the Lord has put before them. You know that for sometime Dr. Cox has been using his chiropractic work to further...the ministries of many other Christian workers across Europe. While he was working directly with the Trans World Radio station, he was receiving a salary, and so he donated his chiropractic work to further the Gospel.

"...the Lord has been opening up fantastic opportunities in France for Dr. and Mrs. Cox to work with Catholics...Priests and nuns are coming to Bible studies. As you know, the Catholic/ Protestant issue is still rather touchy in some places. [Therefore] the Coxes have given up their job with the radio station in order to protect the station in case there would be some backlash in the community because of his work with the Catholics. They still help the radio station in an unofficial way, but feel they should pursue this open door for the sake of the Gospel while it is open. So they receive some money for doing odd jobs with the station, but I am sure that it cannot be enough to meet their needs as they travel to help other Christian missionaries.

"Clark and I personally have seen our work with students increased since we have been going to Dr. Cox. Naturally as soon as we learned that he needed support we began to think how we could begin supporting him. I am not sure what the Lord will have you do with this information, but we knew you would like to know and would know others who would be interested. (The Coxes do not know we are writing to you.) You can be proud of them. They represent the Lord first and then your profession very well." (Pedicord, Campus Crusade, 1976.)

The Christian Chiropractors and various individual doctors sent funds and equipment to support the Coxes' ministry as they were able.

Another Generation Joins the Ministry

In 1981 Dr. David and Phyllis' daughter Mayda graduated from Canadian Memorial Chiropractic College in Toronto and returned to Monaco to enter into the ministry with her parents.

That summer, Drs. David and Mayda Cox went to Hungary (then behind the Iron Curtain), and Dr. Dave spoke to a group of Baptist pastors. Both Drs. Dave and Mayda provided chiropractic care to everyone who attended; it was the first time most of them had experienced chiropractic. From there the two went on to Germany to another pastors' conference and did the same thing, helping pastors and missionaries both spiritually and physically.

In 1983 Dr. David wrote about his work with Campus Crusade:

"I was invited to Campus Crusade for Christ's European Directors Conference in Aldelboden, Switzerland. There were directors and their wives from13 [European] countries...Most of the directors and their wives took advantage of my services.

"Campus Crusade should be commended for their high valuation of chiropractic care for their staff. The European Director ... wants it available for his staff if they so desire...the wives were especially appreciative because they usually do not get included.

"Following that week I went on to Germany to the Black Forest area where Campus Crusade has their European headquarters. There I gave chiropractic care to their staff, and also to the teachers and students at the Black Forest Academy. I saw between 50 and 60 patients a day in these three locations. It truly was a special privilege to serve the body of Christ in this way. I am so thankful that our daughter Dr. Mayda is now able to take care of my patients at home while I am away."

Dr. David and Phyllis continued their work in Monaco; however, due to the ill health of David's sister and mother in Newport Beach, California, they traveled back and forth many times and spent considerable time ministering to them until they died.

Then, on July 16, 1997, Dr. David Cox died of liver cancer. He had few symptoms until it was too far advanced to operate, and he was rushed to the hospital in Monaco where he died. Phyllis has moved back to Costa Mesa, California, and is continuing her witness for the Lord in a Bible teaching ministry.

With little support from any home organization, Dr. Dave and his family had a wide-reaching ministry in chiropractic, radio engineering, and Bible smuggling and distributing throughout Europe. He served against all odds...but God.

Bolivia, Mexico, Ecuador
Dr. Stanley Lindblom

Dr. Stanley Lindblom of Plentywood, Montana, spent six weeks in the summer of 1965 in Window Rock, Arizona, working with Dr. Dinah VanDyken and the Operation Navajo Project. Dr. Dinah wrote about Dr. Stanley's service:

Dr. Stanley Lindblom

> *"The Navajoes felt at home with him, as he has a quiet way that appeals to them. They could feel that he has genuine interest in them and their welfare. Missionaries here also felt drawn to him."*

August 1, 1965, Dr. Stan indicated that he would like to work with the Johnsons in Bolivia for a short term. Dr. Lindblom's brother had joined his practice in Plentywood, and, as Dr. Lindblom was single and had no family obligations, he felt the call to serve the Lord in short-term chiropractic missions. His work with Dr. Dinah Van Dyken had whetted his appetite for more mission activity.

Dr. Stan had a wide-ranging and effective ministry during his months in Bolivia. When he left, Dorothy praised his ministry:

> *"We miss [Dr. Stan] very much because he had endeared himself to the hearts of all–missionaries, Bolivian Christians, high-class folk, and the humble Indian. He always showed God's love and his own personal...concern for them–whether through chiropractic adjustments, advice, prayer, singing in the choir, going out to the country areas to reach the lost, or just chatting.*
>
> *"He seemed to understand and respect the patterns of culture in Bolivia, and it is for this reason the Christian brethren and his beloved patients were saddened by his departure. They truly loved him.*
>
> *"His presence here lent color as well as prestige to the mission. Dr. Stan and Dr. Bridge had many good discussions together about various cases and new techniques. Indeed, he was a tremendous help and encouragement to Dr. Bridge, and through his cooperation, the X-ray is now functioning.*

"He encouraged us to expand the work. While he was here, the country work became a reality, souls came to know Christ, and more patients found relief for their ailments and some came to know the true physician. There were few indeed whose lives he has not touched. It was the Christian Chiropractors Association who took care of his traveling expenses. This fine organization is comprised of dedicated Christian doctors with the divine motivation of promoting chiropractic in the mission fields of the world.

"Dr. Lindblom gave his sacrificial services to the Lord and to Bolivia and to us without remuneration. We can never truly repay him but we know that the Lord can, and we pray that he will be richly used of the Lord wherever He leads."

Dr. Stanley Lindblom may have blessed the Johnsons and their work in Bolivia, but Dorothy Johnson had a special ministry to him too. Shortly after Dr. Stan arrived in Bolivia, we received the following letter from Dorothy:

"We like Stan 'heaps' for he is a godly man and loves souls. It is such a relief to have him here to help and also to give adjustments to Dr. Bridge. Tell me, Dr. Glenn and MaryLou, how did such a handsome and nice doctor escape marriage for such a long time???????? (Please don't show this letter to him!) We haven't mentioned anything along that line, although in these days I almost feel as though I'm the matrimonial bureau or advisor. So many Bolivians have been coming for help along that line. Should I start on him???? There are some nice girls here - although he hasn't met them yet."

I responded to Dorothy two weeks later:

"Yes, Dorothy, Dr. Lindblom is a handsome and fine fellow, and I am sure that he has had many matrimonial opportunities, but the Lord has never seemed to lead him in that direction. I am sure that the Lord is using him in a greater way now, because he is single, than He could have if he had been married. None-the-less, you use your own judgment as far as playing cupid for him is concerned."

Dorothy wasted no time introducing Dr. Stan to her good friend Lillian Kvamsdal. Lillian had been a missionary in Bolivia with World Mission Prayer League since 1949, working first in the lowlands and then in LaPaz, primarily in children's ministries and in orphanages. On January 4, 1969, Lillian and Stan were married in Swea City, Iowa and Dorothy wrote the following:

"I am sure you are all very happy about Stan's decision to get married to a real wonderful girl. All right, I'm cupid!"

From Iowa to Mexico

Immediately after Dr. Stan and Lillian were married in Swea City, Iowa, they left for Mexico to serve in a school for the blind.

"We had a very nice wedding, the day was also very nice, which we had prayed about for quite a while. It had been stormy for several days before and was very cold and stormy from the day after till we left, and I understand it has not changed too much since.

"We arrived here at Laredo at the Latin American Lutheran Mission where we will be working the next year or so, the Lord willing. We will be working over the border in the school for the blind which was established by Claire Hobart...a blind missionary...[who] has written several works of music and is an accomplished piano artist. [The Hobart family] travels in the summer months...to raise funds for the school and for their work. He has been granted a scholarship by the Lutheran World Federation for the study of Latin American Music at Indiana University at Bloomington and will be leaving the end of this week.

"We will be taking charge of the school...in Nuevo Laredo. We have to pick up the students each morning ...and deliver them home at night. They all read Braille and are quite capable. Some are elderly and have attended for some time, but they get a thorough study of the Bible...The mission center here has a bookstore, church, and three residences; and in the back there is a large and a small trailer. We are at present living in the large trailer house.

"The main language...here is Spanish, although most of the adults can understand English. The school will be in Spanish and of course at first Lillian will have charge as she has spoken it for about 19 years and is very good at it, having taught it...too. I plan to take a course in conversational Spanish at the Laredo Junior College for three nights a week, to get a better ground-work in it. It surely gets away from you if you have not been around it for a while." Sincerely in Christ, Stan and Lillian

From Montana to Ecuador

Following their year of service in Mexico, the Lindbloms set up a chiropractic practice in Sidney, Montana and began an outreach ministry to migrant Mexican laborers. With the support of their Lutheran Brethren Church, they have carried on this migrant ministry for many years.

In September 1995, Dr. Stan and Lillian Lindblom went on a short-term mission to Ecuador. Dr. Stan spent five days taking care of missionaries and their families at the Voz Andes Hospital at the HCJB radio station in their "Good Samaritan Clinic."

While Dr. Stan was taking care of the patients, Lillian shared the Gospel with those in the waiting room. Darlene Johnson, widow of Rev. Morley Johnson, then took the Lindbloms from Quito to her home in Shell, Ecuador, where for the next 4-1/2 days Dr. Lindblom set up clinic in the Moravian church and gave over 300 adjustments.

From Ecuador, the Lindbloms traveled throughout Bolivia (where Lillian had served as a missionary for almost 20 years) visiting missionaries and providing chiropractic care wherever needed. In Santa Cruz, Bolivia, they were impressed with the ministry of C.C.A. missionaries Dr. and Mrs. Ron Firestone.

Dr. Stan and Lillian returned to their Montana home the end of October 1995 to the ministry they have had for many years, that of sharing the Gospel of the Lord Jesus with migrant workers.

Iran
Dr. Harry Kalsbeek

Dr. Harry Kalsbeek of Castro Valley, California, was one of our first members and has consistently over the years been one of our most faithful supporters. Dr. Harry and his wife Lois have been very active in the mission program of their Church, the Redwood Chapel in Castro Valley, California. Dr. Harry has served the Association in several offices, including as President and also as a member of the missions committee.

Dr. Harry & Lois Kalsbeek

Dr. Harry was born in North Dakota but his parents moved to the State of Washington when he was a young child and he grew up there. At the age of two, Harry contracted polio, which affected his right arm and leg, his back and his right hip. Through much perseverance, and exercise, he overcame his disability and was a very active child in athletics. However, at age 17 he fell 20 feet onto his back and was left in a steel brace for twelve months. At the end of that time, he was very weak and had lost his appetite. He was losing weight rapidly. His doctors could do nothing for him. It was at that time that his parents took him to a Chiropractor and he soon began to regain his health. By the end of the school year, Harry was running and playing baseball. In his junior and senior year, he lettered in football, track, and baseball for which he gave credit to his chiropractic care.

After high school, Harry found a job as a sheet metal worker and was sent to Hawaii on Dec. 1, 1941. He was at Pearl Harbor when the Japanese bombed the Harbor and started World War II. He continued working there during the War and returned to marry his college sweetheart, Lois, in 1944. After the War, Harry was working for a car dealer when he again hurt his back. Again he received chiropractic care and this time the young chiropractor talked Harry into going into chiropractic college. He graduated from Palmer School of Chiropractic in 1951 and took graduate work from the California College of Chiropractic in 1953. He practiced in Hayward and Castro Valley,

California for 34 years until his *"semi-retirement"* in 1989, when his son, Brian, took over the Kalsbeek Clinic.

In 1968, Dr. Kalsbeek joined Dr. Glenn Stillwagon and myself on our world survey of missions when we went around the world and visited hundreds of missionaries.

In 1973, Dr. Harry along with Lois and their two daughters, Jan and Elain, left their home and practice in Castro Valley and went to Iran for a year of mission work. Dr. Harry worked in the Kennedy Rehabilitation Center in Teheran where Dr. Flora Colby had been working before she went on to Jerusalem. The Center offered an exceptional opportunity for a Doctor of Chiropractic to work with handicapped children and adults and they set up a chiropractic department in which to work. They only required 14 hours of work per week and the rest of the time could be spent in evangelism and private practice.

This year in Iran was a rather discouraging experience for the Kalsbeeks. The Center, which had been under construction and was supposed to be finished before they arrived, never did get finished while they were there. Added to that Dr. Harry slipped and fell on some ice in January. He wrote:

> *"I had a bad fall injuring my bad right knee, wrist, shoulder, neck and lower back. I crippled around for a while and then felt I should go to see Dr. Cox. We made arrangements, but the flight was cancelled and my back began to feel better, but my knee was in pain. I went to see an orthopedist about the knee. X-Rays showed much damaged tissue so he suggested surgery to clean it up. On Feb 23rd he removed bone fragments, small pieces of torn cartilage, the meniscus and transverse ligament. He did some repair on other damaged tissue and now I trust all will be well. I have quite bad varicosities especially in the right leg. Three days after surgery a clot evidently traveled up and lodged in my right lung, a pulmonary embolism. I had a rough time for about five hours. I thank the Lord for a good heart because the pulse rate was 180 for three hours and 130 for two hours. It felt like it would pound right out of my chest. After 8 or 10 hours they removed the oxygen tube but the IV tube was left in for 60 hours to get the coagulation time right I think I lost about 15 pounds in 9 days. That's good but I am really weak, strength is returning very slowly. I'll soon be good or better than new!"* (April 1974)

Upon their return home, Dr. Kalsbeek filed this report of his year in Teheran, Iran.

> *"On the trip to Teheran we stopped off in Paris and flew to Nice. We spent 9 days with Dr. David and Phyllis Cox and*

family. We were encouraged with their dedication, enthusiasm and the work they were doing. On the way home we stopped in Jerusalem to visit Dr. Flora Colby. Her work also is encouraging.

"The John F. Kennedy Centre for the Rehabilitation of Retarded Children is a private, charitable organization, funded for the entire life of the organization mainly by the Shahnavaz family. The father felt, after 15 years, that the government should assume financial responsibility. The majlis (congress) voted in 1971 to give $125,000 to the Centre. When the representatives of the Plan organization came with the check, they asked for their 20% cut. Dr. Shahnavaz refused to pay off in 1972 and 1973 so the money went into the pockets of the 3 representatives of the Plan organization. This is the reason for the poor financial position of the Centre.

"When we arrived, we were met by representatives of the Centre. We were taken to a christian family's home because they were in California and wanted someone to house-sit for one month. We began looking for housing immediately. Our Iranian friends, whose daughter lived with us for a year, loaned us their second car for a couple of weeks, which was a great help in getting around and learning the City. We also began work at the Centre the first week. We visited the new construction site and were told that it would be completed by October 1973. I noted the progress since my visit in September, 1972 and the speed at which the crew worked and had grave doubts as to the projected completion date.

"Lois was asked to teach four English speaking children, an English girl, a Filipino, an American and an Iranian-German. They ranged in age from 10 to 16 but were of about 2nd grade level in intelligence. There were no materials to work with and very poor facilities, so Lois had to improvise a great deal and, working in an unfamiliar role with retarded children, she had a very difficult year.

"My work consisted of examining each new applicant at the Centre. We made as much of a comprehensive neurological, orthopedic, and chiropractic examination as possible depending on the condition of the child. We determined that over 60% of the cases we saw were the result of endogamy (inter-marriage). Some families had more than one afflicted and in one case, 7 children in one family. They will not use birth control of any kind because they feel that what ever happens is God's will, even when they know there is a good chance for retardation.

"There were two other missionaries working at the Centre. They obtained a work permit for voluntary work and in that manner could qualify for a residence permit so they could stay in

*the country. One was a German RN who was there to work with
the German wives of Iranians. There are over 10,000 of these
ladies, a real mission field. The other is an Afro-American man
from California who had been director of Operation Mobilization.
He was on furlough and working independently.*

*"One of the greatest handicaps we encountered of course
was the language barrier. In my work at the Centre, I was ably
assisted by a psychologist who acted as interpreter when needed.
Her name was Parvin Gharagouzilou*

*"Another real problem was lack of finances and government
intervention and graft. Dr. Shahnavaz would not pay off and this
may result in the complete closure of the Centre. To date, since we
have left, the gratis children have been turned back to the government control which of course has cut the case load a great deal. It
will be interesting to observe the progress of this latest development.*

*"My private practice was not very large but was satisfying in
that I could care for some Americans and Europeans and had
opportunity to introduce chiropractic to quite a few Iranians. I was
accepted by all of the medical doctors I came in contact with, as
an expert in my field. I practiced under the umbrella of the Centre's
license as there is no licensure for chiropractic. There is no word
in the Farsi language for chiropractic so I was known as a spine
and nerve specialist.*

*"Malnutrition is also a very real factor in retardation and in the
care of children at the Centre. Government control plays a large
part in what is available for the children to eat. We were able to
receive some vitamin supplements but it is a very difficult task to
battle customs and other government agencies, to have supplements imported in the country.*

*"We did not accomplish all we intended to do. We needed
more supplements to make a comprehensive study of malnutrition and retardation. We lacked facilities to work properly. The
new building has not been completed and may never be turned
over to the Centre because of political manipulations. I do not
recommend that we consider sending any further replacement until
we see what the outcome of the present situation is.*

*There is a need for Chiropractic, not only in the Centre but in
the country as well. There is a need and a place for the Christian
Chiropractors Association in Iran also. There are not sufficient
missionaries in the country but there is good co-operation between
the different groups working there. The Teheran Bible Church is a
fine evangelical church and there is good opportunity to work there.
The membership consists of people from over 30 different countries. We enjoyed fine fellowship there. They have an outreach to*

foreign as well as Moslem people.

"To summarize, the entire experience was gratifying and educational in many respects. We were disappointed that we could not fulfill the goals we set out to accomplish. We did have opportunities to give witness at various times. My illness provided a good opportunity to demonstrate and express our trust and faith in the Lord. We appreciate very much the backing of the Christian Chiropractors Association members both in prayer and financially and we know that they well be blessed for it." Dr. Harry Kalsbeek 12/74

In the years to come, Dr. Harry and Lois made many other short-term mission trips for the C.C.A. In 1981, he went to the Orient, making stops in Singapore, Malaysia, Philippines, Hong Kong, Taiwan and Hawaii. As Dr. Harry reported the purpose of this trip was to (1) to visit different cultures; (2) to visit mission work and missionaries; and (3) to be of help to anyone who needed his professional services.

Later he went to Ukraine on four more short-term mission trips.

Zaire
Dr. and Mrs. Richard Nymeyer

Dr. Richard Nymeyer graduated from Palmer College of Chiropractic in 1967 and set up practice in Linwood, Washington. But in late 1975 Dr. Rich, his wife Jane, and their three children sold all of their worldly possessions to serve the Lord with Grace Mission of Grand Rapids, Michigan, in Bukavu, Zaire.

After two years of language study in Belgium, they arrived in Zaire to face seemingly insurmountable obstacles including having to cut down trees to make chiropractic tables and office furniture. The Africans knew nothing about chiropractic, but before long they began to give up their pills and witch doctors for the gentle touch of Dr. Rich. He reported seeing up to 50 patients a day. Jane Nymeyer also became endeared to the Africans through her ministry to the women. The Nymeyers spent much of their time trying to develop a mission outreach station in a very remote area of central Africa.

In the Center of Nowhere

"We are in the center of nowhere…[in] the jungle with the only connection to the outside world being by private plane which brings in our mail and [the many] other things that we cannot get down here… We used to have electricity for two hours at night, but tonight it went off after just half an hour, and we were informed by those in charge…that there was only enough fuel to last for a few more days. We need electricity for our lights but also to pump our water.

"…Due to lack of lights, when the sun comes up, so do the people, and so the day starts at 6 a.m. or before. I am at the…hospital or dispensary by 7:30 and after prayer, start working. …[A] male nurse helps keep things moving and also gives injections. I have three adjusting tables that were made here. They are wooden with 2-inch foam padding. They are not much by home standards, but they are

Dr. Richard Nymeyer

adequate. They are all in the same room, separated by half walls, so I don't have far to walk from one patient to another.

"These people are so medically oriented and want a shot for everything including constipation. It has taken some time [for them] to adapt to the chiropractic way of life. I have been treating...between 35 and 40 patients from 7:30-12:30... Sometimes I get done later than that but never too late, as the sun is too hot and only white people and crazy people go out in it...

"The real problem we face physically is that 99% of the people are malnourished, and many, if not all, suffer from worms. I have been amazed at the number of colon and intestinal problems I see after having read about how well off the African was with his high fiber diet. This may be true in some areas where they also eat a balanced diet, but it is not here, and so we see the need for a real nutritional program from the roots up...

"This is a long uphill struggle as we...[try] to understand the people and the conditions under which they have lived. As is always the case, most people are content to stay as they are rather than to change...The real question comes down to a spiritual one of motivation... This is a very fatalistic society, so that is the reason many things we never would be content with are tolerated. Many seem to show no interest when actually they see it as a futile exercise because of tribal custom, which hinders progress, or else it will just be stolen from them, which is also a big problem. Tribal customs are breaking down and the parts that are kept are seemingly the ones that aid the lazy and the thieves. It is a difficult time for these people, and they need help as they adapt and begin to work some of these things out their own way.

"Truly the work here is on the indigenous principle. I am not the director but am more of an advisor, or sometimes I think a goad to make them think, especially in the area of spiritual things. I try to cause them to question whether the way they are living truly glorifies God and matures them for greater and more important responsibilities in this life and next.

"The nurses have asked me to give them some courses on 'everything I know.' ...I hope to gradually change the ideas that are so deeply instilled in them, e.g. that of treating only symptoms, and to look deeper at the cause and what they can do about correcting it either in the hygienic, nutritional, or neurological way. We are also trying...to get them to milk their goats and to eat more eggs and raise chickens to get more protein in their diets.

"We are also trying to raise the status of the women, who now are the 'beasts of burden.' We are trying to get across the idea of making carts that could be pulled by a goat…and to build roads so they could transport the rice and wood from their fields easier than by their back or on their heads.

"Two young men and myself have dug a well and now are planning on building a type of wooden bucket pump to show that wells and pumps can come entirely from local materials… We hope…by example and lots of talking and asking questions to provoke and find the innovators and to also encourage them to do something that will not only benefit themselves but their neighbors…

"In all this we keep returning to the major questions of life: why was I created, what has God planned for me, and am I willing to let God give me what He wants to enable me to do [it] here. As we see more and more the depth and greatness of His answers to these questions in our own lives, we share them with others here, desiring that they might experience them firsthand, all because of and by the power of God…" (Nymeyer, 1976)

Innovations and Hard Work

Dr. Rich taught the Africans how to dig a new kind of well to get pure water and to experiment with solar panels for electrical needs. He developed a generator, foot-powered like a bicycle, to run a Gospel slide show for his patients to watch while waiting in his clinic. During their second tour of duty on the mission field in Zaire beginning in 1979, Dr. Nymeyer wrote the following:

"We received the large box of bandages which you sent…and immediately started to put them to use. Thank you very much. Everything is getting scarce here in the interior. Transportation is a very real problem. We have had a flood in Kindu that is the worst since memory. This has caused us to be cut off from river traffic from Kinshasa. Then with the war in Uganda, there were no goods coming in from the east side of the continent…it takes a long time for supplies to get here due to the huge backlog of goods that need to come. Air traffic is available but cut back due to lack of fuel. If you ever wondered where the end of the world is, we have a candidate here. This has not cut back on the work here as there are plenty of people walking in for care, and we still are the only clinic with medical care in a large area."

Dr. Rich becomes very philosophical as he thinks about his reason for being in this most remote and difficult place.

"It has been impressed on me again recently the endless-
ness of the physical work out here and its limited value in
thinking of eternity. The need for spiritual growth is still the only
thing that will truly change the whole life. Pray for us that we
may have wisdom to provide the most effective program of
personal relationships in which to relate God's Word.

"I have been challenged by critics of missions...that what we
are doing is detrimental to the natives and destroys their relationship to God as they saw Him. In response to that, I remember
an incident of sitting in an African home with a wood fire burning
to take the chill off the air. It was raining hard; the road was a
glistening layer of water over mud and grass. We...had stopped
there because the bridge was out. Discussion was begun as to
whether it was worthwhile to fix the bridge as the road beyond
was equally bad with more bridges in similar shape.

"While...waiting for the rain to let up, we were
interrupted by an elderly gentleman of the Bwami tribe who
came to talk with the 'visitors.' He was of the sect of the people
which, in times past, were the political, social and, in many
cases, the spiritual leaders or teachers...I asked if he would
rather [the white man] had left him and his village alone. His
reply was most interesting.

"He...said in essence, 'We worshipped God in darkness
then. We knew He existed–everyone knows that–but how to
reach Him and how to find out what He wanted of us, we did not
know. We tried different ways. Sometimes they seemed to
get results and other times, no. But then the missionary came
with God's book...and we knew it was God's book because
it was wisdom beyond our wise sayings. God in His book
showed us the way to Him. Before I worshipped God in darkness, but now I can worship Him in light.'" (Nymeyer, 1979)

From the Jungle to the City

Shortly after returning to Zaire for their second term, the
Nymeyers moved out of the jungle and into the city of Bukavu to fill
in for a missionary couple on furlough. Many reasons forced this
move, but jungle life was becoming too difficult.

"I do not jest when I say the work here just about killed me
physically, but I am thankful that it was successful spiritually. We
accepted this move to Bukavu as the Lord's open door to correct
the way we were being rundown physically and having no time
to minister spiritually."

With 500% inflation, it was impossible for their mission to provide the additional allowance to sustain their needs in the jungle. Although cost was still a big problem, some of the necessities of life were available in the city which were not available in the jungle. Dr. Richard also noted that in the city he could work with some strong national pastors who needed his help and guidance. This provided purpose to his move, even though his heart was with the people of the jungle.

> *"We are burdened for our friends in Zaire for their spiritual growth and maturity and the responsibility of living and developing a transformed family life including the physical needs. To meet these needs, we are looking to the Lord for training in family and personal counseling. At the same time, we are [setting] up a corporation that will...[develop or purchase] machines necessary to...[break] the physical slavery to subsistence living in the jungle...The tools necessary would be planting equipment, harvesting equipment,...water pumps and an efficient stove for cooking [and] for purifying water.*

In the end, the political situation and inflation in Zaire combined with the terrible difficulty living and ministering in the area caused the Nymeyers to return to the U.S. Their children's education was another factor. The children would need to go to school over a thousand miles away in Kenya with little opportunity to come home during semester breaks. All of these things together forced the Nymeyers to return to the state of Washington in 1982.

> *"We have resigned from the mission...and plan to make Lynden, Washington our home for the next ten years while our children are in school. We would like to go to Zaire on short term assignments in the coming years as the Lord leads."*
> (December 1982)

Dr. Richard and Jane Nymeyer and their family are examples of sacrifice for the cause of Christ and chiropractic in one of the most difficult areas on the face of the earth. Truly their story is one of *"Against All Odds...But God!"*

Haiti, Zaire, Rowanda, and Beyond
Dr. Deborah Halling

Dr. Deborah Halling is one of the most inspiring missionary chiropractors that the Christian Chiropractors Association has had the privilege to sponsor. Dr. Debbie, from Perry, Iowa, graduated from the University of Iowa and taught elementary school in Georgia and Florida for several years. She completed her masters degree while in Florida, and in 1979 entered Palmer College of Chiropractic. She graduated in 1983 and practiced for a few years in Massachusetts. Dr. Debbie, however, knew that sooner or later the Lord would call her to the mission field.

Dr. Deborah Halling

Ministry in Haiti

Dr. Deborah Halling visited Haiti in 1975 on a short-term mission trip with her church and returned twice in 1985 with an organization called World Harvest for Christ. On the last two trips she visited three villages, riding in old Haitian "tap-tap" buses for eight hours, then transferring to a boat, and finally hiking for four miles.

An advance announcement of the clinic meant that Dr. Debbie arrived to many waiting patients. She carried a portable adjusting table and treated hundreds of Haitian pastors and nationals plus foreign missionaries. Her heart went out to the children, and she and another missionary nurse carried seven of them back to the orphanage in Port au Prince. They were so sick, one died the next day and another in two weeks. Dr. Debbie's heart went out especially to these young ones.

"One little boy had arms and legs swollen twice their normal size. A little girl I cared for had amoebic dysentery and a hemoglobin of four (12-15 is normal). I was able to give a pint of my blood for her. When we arrived at the orphanage, another lady and I bathed them and washed their hair. Patches of skin came right off one little boy's bottom leaving large red areas as I bathed him. Words cannot describe how I felt washing and dressing those little ones and putting them to bed on real mattresses with clean sheets."

This experience stirred Dr. Debbie to give her life for service to those in Haiti who needed her care so desperately. After a couple more short-term visits to Haiti in 1989 and 1991, she went as a full-time missionary chiropractor in 1992. Some of Dr. Debbie's reports were among the most exciting and inspiring of any we have received.

"During clinic...six new malnourished children had to be put into our special home for extended care. Some were listless, swollen, and unable to walk. One little girl died the next day, and I felt such sadness in my heart as I sent the money to have a small coffin built for her. The good news though, is that all the rest are making great improvement and will soon be placed in a feeding program and sent back home to their families. Three small children were rushed to us after sustaining severe facial burns from falling into cook fires on the ground.

"Last week a father [asked] that I take his nine month old son because the mother had died, and he was unable to care for the child. A few weeks before that, a desperate family brought [in] tiny new twins because the mother had been paralyzed in childbirth and was unable to care for them. Please pray for these families that not only will we be able to minister to them by helping the children but also that their hearts will be open to the Gospel.

"The last trip to the far western part of the island was the most difficult one I've ever had. I've seen enough rain and mud to last a lifetime. We were stuck in the mud for hours, had several flat tires, and even rode in the back of several open cattle trucks, arriving home wet and tired in the middle of the night.

"The cattle trucks have high beds with a rope tied to a bar running across the back. To get in, you put one foot up as high as possible on the tailgate and haul yourself up by the rope. One afternoon, as I was sitting in the back of one of those trucks, it began to pour rain. We pulled a tarp...[up to cover] the baggage and people...[but] the tarp was so full of holes that it was almost as wet inside as outside. As I sat there wedged between two others with a washbasin over my head to divert some of the rain, the truck had not one but two flat tires simultaneously. Through the obstacles though, God was faithful and always sent help when we needed it. Despite all the difficulties, many people heard the Gospel, and some were saved." (Halling, 1993)

Dr. Debbie was named "adoption coordinator" for her mission. She loved sharing Christ and caring for the little children. You cannot help being touched by the compassion Dr. Debbie had for those whom she was called to serve.

"A few weeks ago one of my interpreters brought us a child that he had found abandoned in the street. The little boy, whom we named Michael, was about four years old. He could not speak and had a hip deformity from birth that prevented him from walking.

"Little Michael had been lying in the street all day and was covered with dirt. As I bathed him and fed him from a baby bottle, I felt mixed emotions - sorrow for his mother who felt she had to abandon him and thanksgiving that he would never be uncared for again. He slept in my room that night and had a new home by the next day.

"Yesterday was a hard day. A woman came with a big abscess on her abdomen,...another woman's arm...had been burned...in a voodoo ceremony. A two-pound baby was brought in who had been born early that morning. He was premature and very cold. I got to be the incubator, putting him right on my chest under my clothes and covering up with blankets to warm him up. But it didn't work, and he died in my arms. His name was Samuel."(Hallings)

Interim Ministry in Zaire and Romania

The political situation in Haiti was never good, but it became so tenuous in the spring of 1994 that Dr. Halling and most of the other missionaries had to leave the country. But it was not like Dr. Debbie to wait at home for things to calm down. She quickly volunteered to be part of a medical team that Dr. Pat Robinson of the "700 Club" was sending to Zaire to care for the refugees of the war in Burundi and Rwanda.

"On August 8th, I arrived in Goma, Zaire, as part of a medical strike force sent by Operation Blessing, a ministry of the "700 Club"...to bring medical help and relief to the Rwandan refugees. The situation in the refugee camps is grim. Over a million people live in makeshift shelters constructed of broom-sticks, leaves and stalks. Many are covered [only] with tarps given by various relief organizations.

"Although limited food, water, and medical care is now available, there are still over 600 deaths every day. [Our] assault team walks among the refuges locating and transporting those too sick to seek help. My particular group has been assisting in the hospital

and baby care areas and at an orphanage with over 3500
children. My heart has been broken over the suffering of some of
the children in the orphanage hospital.

"Last week, at the place I visited, they were naked, five to a
bed, and too sick with meningitis and dysentery to stand up. Every
day as I feed and clean up a sick child, I feel so honored that God
allows me to help care for His little ones. God willing, I'll be here
for a few months. Please continue praying for me and the Operation Blessing team that we will be protected from accident and
disease and be effective in spreading the Gospel."(Halling, 1994)

Dr. Debbie returned to the States later that year, but only briefly.
Within days she was ministering in yet another part of the world.

"In November, I returned to the United States from Zaire.
Working with the Rwandan refugees was one of the most
challenging and exciting experiences of my life. I'll never forget
a very special young girl that I was able to minister to. After the
cholera crisis took thousands of lives, many children were left
without parents...[and] placed in dozens of orphanages that
sprung up overnight...The director of one of these homes asked
for help with Odetta, a young refugee girl who could barely turn
her head. Odetta would sit staring down without speaking for
many hours at a time. When I attempted to examine her neck,
she winced in pain. After a few sessions of gentle treatment and
prayer, Odetta is now able to rotate her neck from right to left
and easily looks up. Pray that God will continue the healing
process that has begun.

"Just a few days after returning to the United States, I was
invited by Operation Blessing to go to Romania to help with a
medical clinic. For the next week, almost 100 health care
professionals ministered to thousands of Romanians. Each
patient...was personally ministered to by a spiritual counselor.
In Bucharest...our team led 830 people to a personal relationship with Jesus. It was also my great joy to help many Romanians with chiropractic care."(Halling, January 1995)

Return to Haiti

After almost a year, Dr. Debbie was able to return to Haiti early in
the spring of 1995.

"What great joy I have to be back in Haiti. After months of being
away, it is so good to be home. I wish you could have been here
to see my reception at the orphanage...I was nearly pushed
down by the mob of little ones that surrounded me, all wanting
hugs and kisses.

"The U.S. military have been very kind to the children in our orphanage, helping to protect them because our compound is so close to the airport. The most memorable day was when a big helicopter hovered over our property and landed right in the yard. Some of the soldiers had found an abandoned child and literally dropped him into our care. This Friday they are returning again, this time bringing a big celebration meal for all of the kids to share.

"Yesterday I returned from a trip out into the mountains to visit one of our clinics and the home for malnourished children. What an experience! The first night I stayed with two Haitian girls in their home. They gave me a wonderful bed, and I was so grateful after a long day on the road. Not two minutes after the lamp was out, I was suddenly fully awake again. Rats were everywhere scratching and knocking over things in the house. The Haitian girls just slept through it all. Was I ever glad to see morning come!

"You all should be here. It's 90 degrees in my room and no electricity so no ceiling fan. It has rained only once since I've been here the past month, so our cistern is getting very low. This morning I instructed the workers to draw the rainwater that has collected over the past several months in our never-used swimming pool, strain it through a towel, and use for washing and toilet flushing. It is a little green, but the tadpoles love it.

"I have had many chiropractic patients, some new, but many I've had in the past. The most common complaint I get is headaches with neck pain and chronic low back pain. It is such a joy for me to care for them."(Halling)

In the early 1980s, Dr. Glenn Stillwagon made several short term visits to Haiti; and in 1984 he had stationary Thompson adjusting table delivered to Haiti. It was left with a pastor in a village some four hours north of Port-au-Prince, and we arranged with him to have the table brought to Port-au-Prince for Dr. Halling to use. Unfortunately by the time she received it, the table needed major repairs and all new cushions. This was taken care of, and Dr. Debbie wrote, "My new table - the one that was resurrected from the dead - is now in full use." This greatly aided her ability to provide quality chiropractic care to her Haitian patients as well as to the dozens of missionaries that she treated at her home in Port-au-Prince.

Dr. Debbie also reached out to minister in the women's prison.

"Last week I had the privilege to begin ministry at the women's prison. Along with several Haitian Christians, I rode

downtown in the back of a pick-up. It couldn't make it up one of the steep hills, so we walked the rest of the way, winding through some poor neighborhoods until we reached the prison.

"We had a service with about thirty ladies out in the court-yard of the prison under a tree. We were separated from them by huge rolls of razor wire almost as tall as a person. During the singing and preaching, I watched their faces through the wire. Some had no expression, a few were crying, and one young woman let out blood-curdling screams. Later during prayer time, that same lady wept in my arms.

"The guards let those who wanted salvation or healing walk around the barbed wire to us at the end of the service. During the prayer time, I also got to pray with Chantal, a fourteen-year-old prostitute who gave her heart to the Lord. Two others like her also received salvation. Some of the ladies' situations are desperate.

"Mobile clinic is one of my favorite ways to win people to the Lord, because witch doctors, voodoo practitioners, and demon-possessed people often come for medical and chiropractic help. They won't come to a church service, but they hear the Gospel preached by Haitian pastors as they are waiting to see a doctor. When they come to me for consultation, I give them the Gospel again and often get to pray with them for salvation or deliverance."(Halling, September 1996)

Ministering in the prison was not the only contact Dr. Debbie had with the criminal aspect of Haiti. She shared the following prayer request with the C.C.A. office.

"My big prayer request that I cannot put into my newsletter is...a rash of shootings and break-ins in my neighborhood from the peasant people who live in the ravines close by. I have another missionary woman staying with me at night because she is too scared to stay in her house after an attempted break-in and shooting in her yard. Please pray for our protection and that this violence will stop. One missionary close by was held at gunpoint just recently."

Later she wrote to tell of God's answer to prayer:

"God has answered my prayer about the shootings here in my neighborhood. It still occurs just as much, but my response has changed from great fear to a feeling of security and well being, even when it is loud.

"A few nights ago I heard a bull horn in the road outside. The police were yelling for people to put up their hands and get out of their car. When I heard only silence, I peeked out a window (I had ducked down to the floor), and saw two policemen with rifles and several people with their hands in the air. Instead of being alarmed, I felt relief that the police were there, since they usually won't come. Thanks so much for praying. Please continue. Just knowing the C.C.A. is interceding brings me great comfort."

Dr. Halling's ministry was varied and wide spread. Shortly before leaving Haiti, she summed up her last year there.

"A few days ago I got back from a week in the western part of the island, up in the mountains...I did over 400 consultations for poor Haitians in the area. I had missionary patients waiting for me...when I got back. [My patients] are still amazed that I never charge anyone. When they ask what they owe me I just reply, 'prayer!'

"Another joy for me was getting to preach Sunday night at one of the mountain churches where clinic was held. I've been sharing the Word in the Creole language for three years now, but it is still a constant challenge for me to keep up on new words and to try to get the right pronunciation.

"During the past year, I have had the opportunity to teach Bible school for new pastors and Christian workers here in the city, [to] travel to remote areas to teach at mobile Bible seminars, [to] lecture to Haitian Christian school teachers on classroom methods, [to] speak to Haitian pastors' wives at a retreat, and [to] preach on Sunday in some Haitian churches.

"My missionary patients just keep coming...Some travel from remote parts of the island just for chiropractic treatment. I also treat Haitians who are referred to me. Many don't know the Lord and let me pray for them; and some even request prayer on subsequent visits. Besides this, I teach at missionary day schools in English from time to time, substituting when the regular teacher is out as well as teaching remedial math and reading."(Halling, October 1998)

A New Ministry in A New Land

In May 1999 Dr. Deborah Halling left Haiti was reassigned by the Foreign Missions Board of the Assemblies of God to a ministry in Asia. Because the country is closed to Christian missions, she does not want her location published, but she writes the following:

"The new country, which is closed to missionaries has many abandoned children who need love and care. My great desire is to work with these children, much like I did in Haiti. It will take a lot of preparation–spiritual, financial and educational–but God is able and will bring everything together. Since I am not allowed to enter as a missionary, I will go as a teacher, doctor, and even as a student.

"...After language school [I may] teach English in one of the many universities. In this way, I can develop friendships and share the Gospel casually as students see the difference in my life. Since I will be a guest in this foreign land, I will respect their laws and allow God to use me within that framework. As much as I miss Haiti and my special friends there, my heart is overflowing with thanks to the Lord for His new opportunity of ministry"

A few months later, Dr. Debbie wrote from her new home:

"The only way that I can win the friendship of these people at the university where I am teaching and studying is through common interest and service that I can offer. This is where my chiropractic skills will be vital. I believe I am the only chiropractor in this country. As in the past, I will be treating patients at no charge. During my time in Haiti, this meant thousands of patient visits in my home or in clinics all over the island. My portable tables were literally torn apart by the constant transporting on trucks, boats, and the tops of people's heads. They were repaired so many times that the bottoms were full of holes where new screws were driven.

"Thanks to the C.C.A., I have a beautiful new portable table...I will be using it to treat many other 'missionaries' who need chiropractic care...those already working in this area...are thrilled that a chiropractor is here. In Haiti, the chiropractic care I gave a fellow missionary kept him on the field instead of having to return to the U.S. for extended treatment. God willing, I will be able to do the same while I am here.

"In addition to fellow expatriates, I will offer chiropractic care to the students I teach, children I care for, and the professors...at the university where I am studying and teaching. I may also get to lecture on chiropractic at a local medical school. Since allopathic treatment is not popular here, they will be open to chiropractic. I am already praying that the Lord will use chiropractic to open many doors and give me favor with government officials. This is critical for me, since all ministry opportunities in local areas come through personal relationships with these officials."

This was a tremendous change for her–new culture, new language, much farther from home–but still working in an orphanage, using her chiropractic care and witnessing for her Lord in a more subtle and quiet way. She requests that we do not disclose her whereabouts, but we do speak with her regularly. She assures us she is having a great ministry, and God is using her and blessing her ministry immensely. Against all odds...But God.

Honduras and Bolivia
Dr. Bruce & Katie Kniegge

Dr. Bruce Kniegge's chiropractic practice in Anchorage, Alaska, was thriving when he, his wife Katie, and their two sons took a different kind of vacation in 1983. They went to Quito, Ecuador, for seven weeks of ministering to the health needs of the missionaries and nationals in that South American country. The pleas of the missionaries for them to return sparked the Kniegges' interest, and they began to ask what the Lord would have them do.

Dr. Bruce & Katie Kniegge

"It all began at my salvation in 1972; I knew...God wanted to use me for His service. The Holy Spirit...called me, even though I did not know all He wanted me to do or even much about the new life in Christ. But discipleship through the Navigators and encouragement from... the Christian Chiropractors Association as a student at Palmer College of Chiropractic helped that 'call' seed grow. I was amazed...[to] read about Dr. Larry Garman in Peru and knew even more, God was giving me the excitement of serving in missions as a chiropractor also.

"After my graduation from Palmer in 1976, I wanted God's will for my life and practice. After being voted into the Christian Chiropractors Association...Board of Directors in 1978, the excitement grew as I heard the stories of doctors who had gone on short-term mission trips.

"In 1983, my family and I...[made] our first short term mission trip to Quito, Ecuador. We spent seven weeks providing chiropractic care to missionaries, their families and a few national workers. WOW! What a trip! Not only did we have a great time helping hundreds, but the permanent 'CALL' was established.

"At that time I had a practice in Alaska. We made every effort to figure out how to get out of debt...[and] go full time into missions. My heart's goal was not only for me to go as a chiropractic missionary, but...to encourage others in our profession to do the same...working at the home office would be a good start.

"In 1989 the [C.C.A.] Board of Directors...voted to have me...establish a Mission Director's office. It was a pleasure, and

in two years behind the Mission Director's desk much new excitement was sparked to member doctors. However, my dream was to be out in the mission field as a 'hands on' doctor sharing the Gospel...

"I think of the song, 'It only takes a Spark to Get a Fire Going.' God has led [C.C.A. doctors]...to share the Gospel through health care in an ever-needy world. I am so glad that God called me to help [start] the C.C.A. program, and many doctors are enjoying the fun of serving and living that life that says, 'thank you.'"

Ministry in Honduras

After several more short-term trips to Central and South America, the Kniegges joined Global Outreach Mission in 1994 as full-time missionaries to Honduras. Dr. Kniegge converted an old school bus into a roving clinic and served hundreds of people in the remote mountains and valleys of southern Honduras. Their health ministry provided chiropractic care as well as basic health education, first aid, and over-the-counter type medical service in these remote villages.

In 1996, their first full year of service, the Kniegges reported sharing the gospel with 4760 people and seeing over 100 make first-time decisions for the Lord. They distributed thousands of tracts and worked closely with national pastors in church building and development.

A Bullet to the Head

On January 21, 1998, Dr. Bruce picked up Dr. Phillip Yoo from the San Pedro Sula airport. The C.C.A. member from Illinois planned to work with Dr. Kniegge for few weeks. Because the plane was late, it was dark before they left the airport. Also in the car were three Honduran nationals and a patient of Dr. Kneigge returning from surgery in the U.S. The car was loaded with luggage and over 70 pounds of vitamins that Dr. Yoo had brought for distribution to needy patients. They knew as they started their 2-1/2 hour drive that roving gangs of bandits made the situation dangerous.

As they left the main highway, a pickup truck suddenly forced them off the road, and two gunmen jumped out shooting. One shot hit a rear tire; another struck Dr. Bruce in the head

"The bandit pointed the gun at my head and pulled the trigger. My head was thrown back, and then I slumped as blood began pouring out on my shirt. I thought I was dead and was waiting for the presence of Jesus."

One robber demanded Bruce's wallet. Realizing that he had some important papers in his wallet, Bruce gave him some money and threw the wallet on the floor. The robber moved to the back of the car where his comrades were unloading the trunk; Bruce stepped hard on the accelerator and drove to a hotel a few blocks ahead.

At that point three of the passengers were left off. Dr. Yoo took over driving as the final passenger tried to stop the bleeding and care for Bruce in the back seat. The bullet had gone through his left eye socket and lodged in his nose.

The Siquatepeque Evangelical Hospital was still several miles away. The tire that been shot gave out and the last two miles had to be driven on the wheel's rim. At the hospital, Dr. Bruce received emergency care and was flown to Houston where his left eye was removed along with the bullet, which had lodged dangerously close to the brain. For most of us that would be the end of the missionary story...BUT GOD!

After three weeks in Houston, Dr. Bruce and Katie returned to Honduras to continue their mission work. By the end of 1998, the stress from all that had happened took its toll, and the Kniegges returned to the States for an extended furlough. In the meantime, a hurricane devastated Honduras making it nearly impossible to return to their mission home.

Ministry in Bolivia

"During this time on furlough we have been praying intensely about a return to God's service in the foreign field. We wanted God's will for our lives and His only. Going back to Honduras was just not in the plan because of the turmoil and stress created there. So if we were to return to another mission field, God would have to open the door. And He did!

"Out of the blue, as we would call it, Dr. Ron Firestone, a missionary chiropractor whom we had worked with briefly while on a short-term trip to Mexico City, wrote me...He and his wife are bi-vocational [missionaries] in Santa Cruz, Bolivia, South America. He is director of the mission hospital, and he invited Katie and I...to work in the hospital. I would [direct] the chiropractic department and Katie [work] as a dental assistant and administrative assistant in the management of the hospital...

"After an exploratory trip down to Bolivia and a report to my mission, Global Outreach has...appointed us to serve in Bolivia. How wonderful to be invited to serve our wonderful God and Savior again." (Kniegge, January 2000)

In Santa Cruz, Bolivia, Dr. Bruce worked in the hospital with Dr. Firestone as well as in several out-patient clinics in the countryside. Samaritans Purse, the relief arm of the Billy Graham Association, helped deliver a container of supplies to the Kniegges which included a Thompson adjusting table, an x-ray machine, some therapy equipment, hospital supplies and vitamins. (C.C.A missionary Dr. Robert N. Thompson had been deeply involved with Samaritans Purse during his lifetime.) Dr. Bruce bought a four-wheel drive, diesel, double-cab truck for his transportation into the outlying areas:

"I am working 4 days a week in the hospital along with Dr. Rusty Firestone (Dr. Ron Firestone's son–ed.)...Dr. Ron Firestone is the hospital director,...teaches at the university with his wife, Violet,...[and has his] own private chiropractic clinic on the other side of town...Bi-vocational missions has been Dr. Ron's passion for many years, following the Biblical example of Paul. The hospital sees about 2000 patient visits per month, and I saw another 500 in the chiropractic department. It [also teaches] nurses and laboratory students from the Evangelical University. This university has about 2800 students.

"Our ministry includes...seeing about 500 patients per month and about 75 new patients per month...[and] we go out once per month to a village where there is little or no dental, medical, or chiropractic care. We work out of a local village evangelical church, as there is follow up for new decisions in Christ.

"[At] the last place...I saw 210 new patients in one day and a total of 329 for 2 days...The spiritual ministry was handled by the pastor, and I don't know the number of decisions. But he assured me there will be plenty, as he visits each [person who] came to the clinic. Because his gift is one-on-one evangelism [he] will be able to lead many to the Lord. We gave him enough work for an entire year of visiting.

"...[In a church] a few weeks ago...I gave my testimony about being shot in Honduras and how I was ready to meet the Lord...I asked, 'Are you ready to meet the Lord if you were to die today?' ...17 people trusted in Christ after the invitation was given. Wow! Thank you Lord."

Ministry with Students

Both Palmer College of Chiropractic in Davenport, Iowa, and Parker College of Chiropractic in Dallas, Texas, have sent teams of senior students to Bolivia to work with Dr. Firestone and Dr. Kniegge. Dr. Bruce told of a visit by a Palmer team in October 2000:

"Wow! We just [saw] the Palmer College team fly away. A total of 25 students and 5 instructors were here along with my good friend and supporter Dr. Willard Smith. Dr. Willard just retired after...40 years at Palmer...He has such a great way with students and patients.

"These students are in their senior year of clinic and this experience of seeing 3840 patients in six and a half days was fantastic. All the attention this created in the community was unbelievable. Four television stations, two radio stations, along with 3 newspapers, came to interview, film, and experience treatments themselves. We had about 50 volunteers from the community, both secular and missionary, to help translate... organize the lines, and help patients fill out paper work. There were pastors doing counseling...and every time I walked by their table, they were praying with or counseling someone. Christian tracts were given out to all, and we pray the impact both healthwise and spiritual will continue to be fruitful.

"Katie and I worked 12 hours or longer [while] the team was here but it was worth it. Several instant cures were seen after treatments, with happy faces...and appreciation....

"We had opportunity to share with about 20 of them at our house one evening over pizza and dessert. I shared...how they, too, could use their skills in foreign countries because there is such a need here, and there are too many chiropractors in the States. I also shared about the shooting incident in Honduras when I thought I had died from the bullet in the head. Being ready to die is something we all need to do, but some don't want to think about it. We hope it had a lasting impact on their hearts..."

At the end of the Kniegges first year of service in Bolivia, Dr. Bruce summed up his ministry in this way.

"We spent our first 6 months [in the Evangelical Boliviana Hospital] ministering to the poor and not so poor...The word gets out so that people from all walks of life hear about the wonderful help there is in chiropractic. The hospital benefited...because they charged according to [a patient's] ability to pay...the richer patients helped cover the overhead for the poor. Each patient was given a tract...and we had the opportunity to counsel many with spiritual and other domestic problems.

"...[We also] did outreaches with some of the hospital staff into villages as close as 5 hours and as far as 12 hours away... The long drives over rough roads, sleeping on hard floors, and *eating food we are not use to eating, was well worth the new souls for the Lord.*

"The second 6 months [we changed] from the hospital setting to more outreaches and working in local orphanages...

"So now we care for 300 children in 6 different orphanages and the Cerebral Palsy center...we still do the outreaches but with different doctors and dentists. We also support with chiropractic care local pastors and missionaries from many different missions.

"Katie has had fun...with several different ladies Bible studies with new believers. Some have never cracked open a Bible in their lives. She is excited to see them grow and has led several in the believer's prayer as they were not sure if they had ever trusted in Christ.

"I have become the new leader in a men's Bible study and a monthly men's prayer breakfast outreach to the English speaking community."

"The Truck that Swims"

Dr. Bruce made many trips into difficult areas on his village outreach program including the time he calls "The Truck that Swims."

"We had some heavy rains last month and a Quechua Indian village about 160 kms. from Santa Cruz was under water...Their beds were bamboo poles, about two inches in diameter lashed together with long grass braided like rope...The clothes they had on their bodies were patched, and sewn shut so many times that...we would have thrown these rags away years ago.

"...Some people from the local Church of God heard about their brothers and sisters in Christ becoming flood victims. These local poor people took up a collection from many other small congregations and bought food and donated clothing. I volunteered to take it to the victims when no other truck was available.

"Early one morning we packed 1,400 lbs. of food, rice, noodles of various types, potatoes, beans, sugar, flour, salt, and big bags of clothes in my small, double cab Mazda pickup with a short four-foot bed. We had five big men in the passenger part, which loaded the truck to its capacity.

"...We found out that a major bridge had been washed out, and we had to go 100 kms...on a detour...This detour dirt road had large mud holes where only 4 wheel drive could get us through. It took several extra hours ...[traveling] an average of 18 mph. The constant bouncing and jarring to the truck and our bodies really wore on us.

"...The [final] road that went into the temporary village...was

not really a road since no tire tracks had been on it for a while. It was mainly a footpath since the people...were too poor to have cars or trucks...

"I drove to where there was standing water on the road...Our guide got out...to see how deep it was. It was up to his knees. We could see the... path dry again...about 1/8 mile away. There was no other way to deliver these items except to trust God to get us through.

"I prayed and moved forward. It got deeper and deeper. With the diesel engine revving and the super low, 4-wheel drive engaged, I trudged through this water hole. My truck was floating several times as we crossed the pond. We made it to the dry spot, and I stopped.

Now...all I could see was water, real deep to the sides, ...and [more] water in front of us...I couldn't turn around or back up. Forward into more uncertain territory was our only option...I kept the engine revved up and the tires spinning, and we were floating again. The steering wheels acted as my rudder and the spinning tires my propulsion. With a constant prayer on my lips and all our adrenaline pumped at its peak, we made it to the other side...

"The villagers were very happy to receive this...needed food and clothing from their fellow believers in Christ. We unloaded at one of the elder's huts and shared a short about helping others in need sermon with about 20-25 people that had gathered. When the pastor said, "let's pray," my heart was humbled even further as the group knelt in the dirt to praise God for this much needed provision.

"After prayer, I asked if there was anyone suffering from back pain...and I used one of the bamboo slatted beds in the grass hut as my chiropractic table. That is an experience I will never forget.

"It was time to leave and now the truck was 1400 lbs. lighter. I needed some weight to keep it down as close to the road as possible. So we loaded all the people we could into the back, and women and children loaded into the passenger part. Prayer and another miracle got us trough the water again. We said our good-byes and again bounced over the detour caused by the flood...It was without a doubt one of the toughest days I have had...The joy of being a part of this rescue mission was also without a doubt one of my greatest."

Those of us at home are called to pray for those like the Kniegges who are on the front lines in the battle for the bodies and souls of men, women, and children for the Lord Jesus Christ. They battle against all odds...but God.

Columbia
Dr. Jaime Chica

Dr. Jaime Chica, a native of Columbia, South America, with a Doctor of Medicine degree from the Universidad de Valle' Medical School in Columbia, came to know the Lord as his personal Savior through the ministry of Campus Crusade for Christ at the medical school. He served as youth pastor, worship leader, and family group Bible studies leader for the Ekklesia Centro Cristiano Colombiano Church pastored by Rev. Julio Ruibal. In addition to pastoring the church, Rev. Ruibal was a noted South American evangelist, who conducted evangelistic campaigns all over Latin America.

During this time an American family in Columbia with the Colgate Palmolive Company came to know the Lord through the ministry of Rev. Ruibal. Their daughter, Amy, and Dr. Jaime were married in 1983.

Then, while traveling in the U.S. on ministry business, Rev. Ruibal received a chiropractic adjustment. Upon returning to Columbia, he persuaded Dr. Jaime to go to the U.S. to learn chiropractic. In 1985, Dr. Jaime, Amy, and their first child, Janel, moved to the U.S. and he enrolled in the Los Angeles Chiropractic College. He graduated in 1988 and felt the Lord call him to return to Columbia where he would be the only chiropractor in Cali, a city of 2 million people.

The Ministry in Columbia

Dr. Jaime's clinic offered primarily chiropractic care but also medical and naturalistic care. He had a fruitful ministry, and hundreds of people came to know the Lord through his work in the church and in his clinic. In addition, Dr. Chica was soon asked to be an associate pastor to aid Pastor Ruibal.

Rev. Ruibal dreamed of expanding the ministry of the church to include a training school for new believers, especially those from tribal areas, so that they might return to their homes and become spiritual leaders in their communities. He also sought to train his students in hygiene, nutritional awareness, health maintenance lifestyles, and the use of massage and other hands-on therapeutic techniques.

The mayor of Cali, Columbia, was so impressed with this program that he made a government clinic available to the Ruibal ministry and asked that a drug rehabilitation program also be included. Cali, Columbia, was in the area of the country controlled by the international drug cartel, and everyone associated with this ministry knew the dangers in what they were doing. As both Rev. Ruibal's wife and Dr. Chica's wife were Americans, they were especially hated by the drug cartel and were potential targets of their terrorist activities.

The Loss of Loved Ones

On December 13, 1995, as Rev. Ruibal prepared for a meeting with other pastors of the city, revolutionary terrorists rang the bell to his front gate. When he answered the bell, Rev. Ruibal was shot in the head and died immediately. After the death of Pastor Ruibal, a prayer meeting was held in the city of Cali. Over 45,000 people gathered, with another 15,000 outside the auditorium, praying for the city and the ministry of the church. A great revival was in evidence.

The church asked Dr. Chica to assume leadership as its senior pastor. Its ministry now included the clinic, a school, a university, a radio station, and television station. This of course, was a tremendous responsibility. Furthermore, being in the center of the country where drug wars were a daily activity, it carried with it extreme danger for all of those associated with the church.

On top of all this, in July 1994 Amy Chica was diagnosed with cancer of the ovaries and colon. Surgery revealed that it was too far advanced to help, and she was given only two months to live. At the time they had four children, age ten and under. She lived until July 11, 1996. Amy's body was returned to America for burial.

Returning to Columbia

Dr. Chica spend a couple of months in Florida contemplating how he could manage his clinic, the church and all of its related ministries, and raise four young children by himself. He pleaded with the members of the C.C.A. for another chiropractor to help in his clinic. Then he returned to Cali, Columbia, to take up his ministry again.

"Coming back to Cali was difficult. Many memories of Amy were all around us. Little by little, we grew accustomed to the fact that she is with Jesus. It is still going to take some time, but the Lord is good and merciful. The kids are adjusting well.

Dr. Jaime Chica Family

"I have a Brazilian girl helping me with the children during the hours I am not at home. My involvement in the church is more than ever. In the afternoons, I work in my clinic; and in the evenings, there are meetings and times of ministry. I have to work hard to find time with the children.

"The church is strong, and the people are committed. There is excitement...as we look forward to what the Lord is about to do. The leaders are...[re-evaluating] the entire scope of the ministry. With Pastor Julio gone, changes needed to be made.

"This has been such a hectic year for me, I have had to put things on hold as I recuperate and seek the Lord. Now I have been refreshed and refilled with the Spirit and purpose of God. I am ready to meet the challenges of spreading the Gospel and ministering to the needs of our city. Pray that this time of reorganization goes smoothly. I only want to bring glory and honor to Jesus in everything I do.

"I ask that you continue to not only pray for me, my family, and the church, but also for Columbia as it is at a critical cross-road in her history. The guerrilla forces have really stepped up their efforts to overthrow the government forces. There is even talk of declaring a state of war. God has placed me here at a most opportune time...Pray that the people would be open to the true message of our loving Savior. Pray that the church works hard to meet the challenge.

"Thank you for your love and support...Dr. Jaime Chica"

The man who had assassinated Rev. Ruibal escaped from jail. He and his gang were committed to destroying the ministry of Dr. Chica and the church. After Dr. Chica testified in court against the man, the threats on his life became constant and more severe. It was impossible for him to go outside without bodyguards.

In January 1997 he married the Brazilian woman who took care of his children. At that time he felt drawn to leave the country for the sake of the children, but the Lord said, "Not yet!" The threats on his life grew more intense each passing week. Finally he was again asked testify in court against the man who shot Rev. Ruibal on March 28, 1998. On March 29 he and his family left everything behind in Columbia–his practice, his home, his church, everything.

The Chicas moved to St. Petersburg, Florida, for several months and then to Virginia where, at the time of this writing, he is practicing chiropractic. He has never lost his love for his home country, but until the Lord prepares the way again, it is not possible for him to return to Columbia.

Jamaica
Dr. Angella Roberts

Dr. Angella Roberts (D.C.) and her husband, Dr. Joseph Roberts (Th.D.), had been married for many years and their two children were grown when the Drs. Roberts left in January 1996 for Mandeville, Jamaica.

Dr. Angella Roberts

In addition to her degree from Life Chiropractic College, Dr. Angela had Child Evangelism Fellowship training plus one year of Bible college. This training prepared Dr. Angella not only to establish a chiropractic mission outreach but also to assist Dr. Joseph in starting a new church, opening a Bible institute and seminary, and establishing an umbrella organization to take advantage of other ministry opportunities. They have also helped with many C.C.A. short-term missionary teams. Theirs was a varied ministry.

"I thank God for the work that I have in Jamaica as a doctor and as a missionary's wife as well. My work as a doctor enhances my work as a missionary's wife because I have the opportunity to meet and minister to many people that I would never meet only as a missionary's wife.

"I have patients that are very poor, but I also have patients that are in the upper class of Jamaican society and business. This allows my husband and I to have a much broader ministry than the average missionary [does]. We might be with CEO's and politicians one day and then the next day be with the 'common bush people'..., and yet minister to both. I believe that we are learning what Paul meant when he wrote about 'becoming all things to all men that he might win some.' It also broadens my perspective about the Jamaican people in a way that I never dreamed would ever happen."(A. Roberts)

In August 1997 the Roberts' son was attacked with a pick ax to the head, nearly killing him. After many hospital stays, he finally returned to the U.S. to complete his recovery.

Adding to this difficulty was a worsening economic situation in Jamaica. Soon Dr. Angella's patients could no longer pay for their care, and she could no longer pay rent for her office. It became increasingly difficult for the Roberts to carry on their ministry. In December 1999 they returned to Florida. Dr. Angella got her Florida chiropractic license, and they set up a "base camp" from which to continue their work in Jamaica.

During their five years in Jamaica, the Drs. Roberts saw over 600 professions of faith, many baptisms, yearly vacation Bible schools and youth camps, and Dr. Angella treated hundreds of patients. Even working from their base camp in Florida, Dr. Angella reported in January 2001 that the Jamaicans no longer them consider them "Americans" but "Jamaicans."

New Guinea
Dr. and Mrs. Keith McKim

In June 1986 Dr. and Mrs. Keith McKim, from Nampa, Idaho, and their three small children were assigned as Nazarene church missionaries to the Wycliffe Base at Ukarumpa, New Guinea. They were primarily to serve as house parents in a youth hostel. They had ten teenagers for whom they were responsible–children of missionary parents who were working in Wycliffe translation out-stations.

While on the field, Dr. and Mrs. McKim were blessed with their fourth child, Kaysha. With four children of

Dr. Keith & Jana McKim & Family

their own, all under eight years of age, and ten missionary teenagers, the McKims had an exciting ministry right in their home. However, Dr. Keith still had time to continue his chiropractic service as well.

> *"... I have opportunity to treat people from just about every continent. There is a large influx of expatriates due to missionaries and international businesses. I am always pleased to see the positive impact our profession is making on the world. Most are familiar with the benefits of chiropractic. The national people are not as aware of the profession, but the word of mouth, as always, carries the message rapidly.*

"The referral relationship with many of the medical profession is very open and friendly. The atmosphere and attitude within the health care field seems to be 'if it works and helps the patient, let's try it.' It has been my pleasure to treat patients in one of the hospitals on occasion. I believe the openness of mind is possible because political and financial barriers are relaxed. Plus, many of the professionals are missionary volunteers who have nothing to gain, only a service to give. It is encouraging to see that it is possible for the two largest health professions in the world to cooperate for the benefit of mankind." (McKim, 1987)

"Many of the conditions that I treat are from...under use [or] over use. The Bible translators tend to do a lot of sitting at computers or talking with the national people. Then they might be required to hike out to a village or exert themselves in some way and end up with an injury. I have [tried] to get many of the translators on walking programs. This is not as simple as it might sound. Many of them are in areas where the terrain is very rugged. Others are in areas where people would consider it very strange for a husband and wife to go on a walk together.

"The national people tend to work very hard and suffer from over use. The women work hard in the gardens all day and carry heavy loads on their heads...The constant physical labor begins to show up frequently in their late twenties and thirties. The major areas of trouble are cervical, lumbar, and knees. Rugby is a favorite sport among the people. It seems that I treat a dozen rugby victims each week...

"My support role as a chiropractor helps the other missionaries to be more productive...in their ministries. [When one Bible translator]...heard there was chiropractic care available [her response] was to cry and praise the Lord. The need for chiropractic care throughout the world is great. I hope to see the Christian Chiropractors Association continue to strive to meet the challenge. " (McKim, 1988)

An unexpected family situation back home forced the McKims to leave their mission post in July 1989.

Malaysia, South East Asia
Dr. Timothy Streit

Dr. Timothy Streit graduated from Palmer College of Chiropractic in 1978, and soon after graduation felt the call of God to serve on the foreign mission field. He attended three years of Bible college in Tulsa, Oklahoma, and went on several short-term mission trips to Guatemala, El Salvador, and Mexico.

In 1988, Dr. Tim began work in the Philippines with Dr. Gordon Heuser and his Trinity Foundation. He trained national health care workers in evangelism and hands-on musculo-skeletal massage procedures. Dr. Tim also, of course, used his chiropractic in taking care of the patients. Dr. Tim also led a team of doctors and evangelists on an outreach crusade during which150 people came to know the Lord in a single day.

This experience gave Dr. Tim the vision of doing a similar crusade in Malaysia for the 21 million people there, mostly

Dr. Tim & Christine Streit

Muslim. In January 1999 he went to Malaysia under Nation to Nation Mission, Int., to teach full time in a Bible school and lead health crusades into the countryside to help meet both the physical and spiritual needs of the people.

Dr. Tim now uses Malaysia as a headquarters to expand his ministry into other areas of South East Asia including India, Vietnam (serving in the underground churches) and Indonesia. His ministry was primarily a preaching and teaching ministry but he uses his chiropractic training when possible.

"...An Indian minister in Malaysia...invited me to come to India. The minister has four brothers and all of them are pastors. One is a pastor in Mysore, and he invited me to preach there in his church. Then every weeknight we went to a different village and held house church meetings. He has 20 villages with house churches in them. I taught in five of them in one week."

"Before I left India last week, I had opportunity to adjust [the wife of one of the dormitory managers]. She is a nurse

teaching other nurses in a medical college in Bangalore...she referred me to the administrator of the hospital who also oversees the employees of the medical school with 2400 employees. I was able to give him some much-needed relief of a cervical-brachial condition he [had been] suffering with for some time. He was pleased, and it may have opened a door for chiropractic there."

On January 1, 2000, Dr. Timothy Streit married Christine David, a fine Christian woman he met in the church in Malaysia. Together they are continuing to minister in Southeast Asia.

Haiti
Dr. Janice Lambert

Dr. Janice Lambert was practicing chiropractic in Sacramento, California, when the Lord called her and her husband to Haiti. Glen Lambert had been an executive with the New York Life Insurance Co. The first two years in Haiti, they were involved in film and visual aid evangelism.

Dr. Janice & Glen Lambert

Then in 1988, Mission Aviation Fellowship appointed them as missionary evangelists to bring the JESUS film, prepared by Campus Crusade for Christ, to thousands throughout the island. With the help of MAF, Glen Lambert, a gifted speaker and evangelist, also held evangelistic crusades throughout Haiti and the Dominican Republic. Dr. Janice, in addition to working with her husband's evangelistic work, continued her health ministry.

"...It was [well known]...that I was a chiropractor...I was flown to Port-au-Prince to take care of an MAF pilot who had a severe back problem. I took care of numerous elite Haitians, and hundreds of peasants, right outside my door, in my outdoor clinic, which was on my patio. I have no x-ray unit, and the only instrument I have is an old NCM type instrument. I used palpation extensively, leg check, and motion palpation. The results were fantastic. I used Grostic technique without x-rays and some full spine technique. Because of my previous training, I also administered a tremendous amount of first aid." (Janice Lambert, 1988)

Brazil
Dr. and Mrs. James Olszewski

Dr. James and Christy Olszewski, their three sons and two daughters (ages 0 to 11) lived in Winchester, Kentucky, until God called them to serve in Brazil with Call to the Harvest Ministries. So in the summer of 2001, Dr. Jim opened a chiropractic clinic in Manaus, Brazil, on the Amazon River in northern Brazil.

Dr. Jim Olszewski and his wife, Christy
Children: L to R: Spencer, Kalista, Malachi & Aundrea
Not shown: Heisman, born August 31st, 2002

"Friends and family members could not understand...this drastic decision to move to Brazil. This gave me an opportunity to tell...how the Lord was the reason for us leaving Kentucky. Everyday, I was able to share my experience with someone different - Christian and non-Christian. I was sharing more about Christ in six months than I had done in 15 years.

"There was no longer a barrier or fear factor. I was bursting at the seams to tell as many people as possible about how my Lord was making it possible for us to go to Brazil to do His work. I considered it a miracle, and that is how I expressed it to others. This sharing experience continues even after I arrived here in Manaus...

"I never knew life could be so good. What a privilege it is to be serving God here in Brazil...He has carried me through the tough times, and He has stood by me through my triumphs... moving [the] entire family to another country was the hard part. Now I understand why. The Lord has rewarded us with an overwhelming sense of joy!

"Yes, I miss my family and friends back home...things are not always perfect, but there is something in the air...It is the presence of our All Mighty God...I knew it was His will for us to be here...His angels were working overtime to make sure every last detail was taken care of...I am so excited how God is using us.

"...The chiropractic clinic is growing and the waiting room is

packed with patients sitting on the floor and in the hallway. I saw 180 patients last week. The most challenging patient so far was a man who was shot in the head. The bullet traveled down through his neck, shattering bones and damaging his spinal cord. He is paralyzed from the neck down. Amazingly though, with each adjustment, he continues to gain strength in his arms and has had some feeling in his legs. We both know that regardless of the final outcome, his true salvation lies with the Lord."

Dr. Jim closes by saying, "Please pray passionately for us!" A further report from Dr. Jim again radiates his enthusiasm to use his professional training to help bring people to Jesus Christ.

"Two weekends ago my wife and I went to a leper colony. While I adjusted, she did some projects with the children...we had a tremendous response.

"Last week we went to a small church in the jungle to do a clinic. The pastor...[told] us not to expect...a crowd, maybe only 15-20 people, which is all that attend on a Sunday. The Lord must have been whispering in their ears. We...[provided] chiropractic care to over 50 people in a two-hour period...

"We have also been working with a school...in a poorer section of the city...being run by one woman out of the kindness of her own heart... There are around 70 kids ranging in ages from 2 to 9 years...whose families do not care whether they attend school or not. They can come to this school...have something to eat, and...be given a chance at surviving...The clinic...[provided] funds to purchase cooking gas. For some time they have had to cook on an open fire....

"[To update you on] the man who was shot and paralyzed, he is able to feed himself and brush his teeth on his own– activities that he was unable to perform prior to coming to the clinic."

Later Dr. Jim wrote the following:

"I have some exciting news. The clinic was featured on prime time news...last week... A group...from the news station [spent] about an hour in the clinic...The phone is ringing off the hook. Today I had 23 new patients walk through the door. That's one way to expand my prayer list. Praise the Lord! We are going to top 225 visits for the week. Can't beat working for the Lord. Every week there is a different reward. It's awesome. It's exciting. It's humbling to experience His mighty power and grace."

At the time of the writing of this book, the Olszewskis have been in Brazil for just over a year, and their continuing enthusiasm is contagious. The C.C.A. is proud to have representatives like them.

Jamaica, Poland, Ukraine
Dr. Charles Jang Dhari

Dr. Charles JangDhari, his wife Kathy, and their family served the Lord as bi-vocational missionaries in Jamaica for four years, and then went to Poland. In Jamaica they chose to self-support their ministry using his chiropractic practice to fund the needs of the family and their Christian outreach. The Jamaican economy made this virtually impossible; therefore, after much prayer, they felt led to Poland in 1996. Kathy explained in the following letter how they have now extended their ministry into Ukraine and Kosovo.

"The clinic here in Krakow remains busy. Dr. Charles and I have also traveled to two other towns in Poland the last two weeks to conduct one-day clinics. It involves…hours in the car, but both clinics were very rewarding.

"The one clinic is in Lubacow in the East of Poland near the Ukrainian border. We have traveled there for two and a half years now. Although my Polish language is weak, it is wonderful to communicate with many of the patients. Somehow, they understand me, and I understand them. One woman…in her eighties…has been our patient for about a year now. She told me…that she had been asking God to send someone to heal her arm for a very long time. After one treatment, she was able to use her arm for the first time in two years without pain. We rejoiced together.

"Our visits to the children's home also continue and are very rewarding. A friend of my sister, from Philadelphia, knitted about 50 sweaters for the children in such beautiful colors. The children were delighted. One little girl looked so beautiful in a pink sweater and was so excited. She hugged me and said she couldn't wait to wear it to school. It was a special delight for me to fit each child and to see the radiant smiles.

"Our Sunday meetings are going well. Dr. Charles is so

Dr. Charles Jang Dhari

faithful in teaching the Word. One new family has been coming since the fall. They lived in Kosovo for 23 years, but returned to Krakow 5 years ago because of the war. The husband is Kosovar/Albanian while the wife is Polish. We met them last summer at the Red Cross refuge camp for Kosovars outside of Krakow. They were the translators for the refugees.

"Charles traveled to Kosovo in January with the husband, daughter, and son. It was a trip from which it has taken some time for him to recover. He had never been in a war zone before, and the effects of hatred of one human being for another deeply affected him. He will be returning to Kosovo the last week of March to conduct a chiropractic health clinic as well as supply some basic health care... So we remain faithful to the call we feel the Lord has on our lives here. (Kathy JangDhari, May 2000)

In addition to expanding their ministry, the Lord has expanded the support base for JangDharis' ministry in Poland. They now receive finacial support from their home church, the Worship Center, a non-denominational Christian organization in Lancaster, Pennsylvania.

Part II

Bi-Vocational
Doctors of Chiropractic
Who Supported their Mission Activity
through their Professional Practice

Bolivia, Mexico
Dr. and Mrs. Ronald Firestone

Both Dr. Ronald and Violet Firestone grew up as missionary kids. Ron's parents served in Bolivia; Violet's served in Mexico. Ron met Violet, a vocational nurse, while he was attending Los Angeles College of Chiropractic.

A Family of Missionaries

In 1974 they joined Ron's parents in Cochabamba, Bolivia, under the Church of God, in Anderson, Indiana. Dr. Ron's father, Dr. Homer Firestone, was an anthropologist and a counselor. He received his Ph.D. from the University of New Mexico and served with the Church of God for fifty years as missionary, mission board member, and leader in establishing the church in Bolivia. He died in 1996. Ron's mother was an R.N. who had learned some manipulative techniques and had a reputation as a great hands-on practitioner. This was just the beginning of the Firestone missionary legacy.

Dr. Ron & Violet Firestone

Dr. Ron's sister, LeTaye, also graduated from Los Angeles College of Chiropractic and, with C.C.A. sponsorship, took graduate work at the Palmer College of Chiropractic. She and her husband, Ray Injerd, also worked with her parents in Cochabamba for several years in the 1970s. Dr. LeTaye wrote the following about those days of ministry:

> *"Each new patient...receives a folder of literature...[in which] the science of chiropractic is explained, and helpful hints are given for everyday health. Then the Word of God is presented in...a paperback Gospel of John and other Christian literature....*
>
> *"Personal testimony is given by the doctors and co-workers to those hungry for the Lord. Our biggest prayer for this clinic is not that it succeeds financially or socially, but that it would be an effective and God-blessed witness of the saving power of the Lord...and that He would use this ministry of health to bring souls into His kingdom. We ask that you pray daily to this end."*

The missionary healthcare legacy did not stop here. Dr. Ron and Vi have two children, a daughter LeMel and a son Homer (named after his grandfather but nicknamed Rusty). Rusty graduated from the Los Angeles College of Chiropractic in 1997 and he, too, returned to practice in Cochabamba, Bolivia.

Bi-vocational Ministries

Over the years the Firestones ministered to over 100 congregations throughout the country. Dr. Ron and Vi often traveled to these churches, speaking and offering health service. Dr. Ron also opened a chiropractic clinic in Cochabamba where he treated up to 100 patients a day.

Dr. Ronald Firestone believes that a missionary should be bi-vocational, and he practiced what he preached. He feels that a missionary should be able to support himself on the mission field; therefore, Dr. Ron has had a successful chiropractic practice while at the same time pastoring churches, teaching school, and doing whatever else was necessary to enable him to carry out his calling.

In 1978 the Firestones returned to the United States for additional education. Vi completed her M.A. in Marriage and Family Counseling and Ron got an M.A. in Nutrition and Psychology. During this time they also pastored a church and opened a chiropractic clinic in the Los Angeles area.

In 1985 the Firestones returned to the mission field, this time to Mexico City where again they pastored a church and opened a chiropractic clinic. Dr. Ron also helped get a law passed to give chiropractic legal recognition in Mexico.

In 1991 the Bolivian Evangelical University asked Dr. Ron and Vi to return to Bolivia to open a school of nutrition, a school of social work, and a school of psychology in conjunction with the university in Santa Cruz, Bolivia. The Firestones organized these schools including developing the curriculum for each one. Dr. Ron was the department head, and both Ron and Vi taught classes. They also opened a chiropractic clinic and counseling center and pastored the only English-speaking church in the area for the next 8 years.

Dr. Ron and Vi continue to work in Santa Cruz, and Dr. Rusty and his wife are in Cochabamba. Dr. LeTaye and Ray returned to California in 1980 where she set up a chiropractic practice and Ray entered graduate school. The three generations of Firestone missionaries is truly a great example of serving the Lord both through the ministry of the Word of God and through ministry of health care, especially chiropractic.

Israel
Dr. and Mrs. John Iatesta

After Dr. John Iatesta graduated from New York Chiropractic College, he set up practice in Portland, Oregon, and taught part-time at the Western States Chiropractic College. Then in 1994 Dr. John and his wife Nancy, with their two daughters Julia and Laura, moved to Jerusalem, Israel. In December 1995, Dr. John wrote the following:

"This...has been a year of blessing for us and also a year of learning about, and leaning on, our faithful Father. We did not anticipate the difficulties–or the miraculous manner in which the Lord has, time and again, seen us through. Just as Peter stepped out of the boat and found himself in...some big waves, we also have had to do what Peter did and reach out for...Yeshua's hand. Praise God, He is always there!

"...We have much to praise Him for. Having said this, I want to thank ...every one of you for...your loving prayer [and] financial and practical support to my family this past year. A very appreciative thank-you for the portable adjusting table which arrived just before Christmas. I know that the Lord has seen your heart and your giving.

"...Since Chanukah ends on Christmas Eve this year, it is natural to blend them into each other. So we are lighting Chanukah candles, and we have our traditional Christmas tree too. It is an opportunity to share about the 'birthday celebration' for Yeshua with our neighbors. What an amazing thing...to see the Chanukah candles burning in the windows of homes and shops throughout the city. Even the hardware store has its Chanukah on the counter as you enter. Chanukah is not in the Bible, but its tradition existed in the Lord's day, and we are told the Yeshua observed it.

"Nancie and I are teaching twice a month at our King of Kings Church...Usually on Fridays, before Shabbot, [Nancie] gets last minute things for the older neighbors and visits with them. Her loving concern for our neighbors has done more to show Yeshua's love than I could ever hope to do. The five brothers who own and operate the local produce market remind me that I am lucky man. I have told them, 'God has blessed me with a wife who loves Him more than she loves me' ...

"As we watch the events unfolding in Israel, we know that the time is so short. May we all see a great harvest for His

Kingdom now. The news is not good here. There is much unrest. Please continue to pray for the peace of Jerusalem. As you do so, may the Lord prosper you."

The unrest did increase, and a few months later, Dr. John described an attack that hit very close to home.

"I was in our kitchen at 6:45 a.m. when I heard what I thought was a sonic boom. It was actually...[a] bomb exploding...approximately two miles away. Apparently, a young Hamas terrorist, dressed as an Israeli soldier and carrying an Army duffel bag containing a bomb, boarded the #18 bus near the Old City. The #18 bus line is one of the longest and busiest in the city. It is our bus running right past our door. We take it, as do many of our friends and neighbors, to go into the city.

"[The passengers we know about personally include] the older brother of a boy and the father of another in Laura's 5th grade class; the older brother of a girl in Julia's 7th grade class; one of two brothers who work in the local electrical store; and a relative of a girl we know who works in the local bake shop. The neighborhood was in a state of shock and mourning. We are hurting with them.

"In the last attacks there was certain 'resolve' that some must be lost so that peace can preserve countless others. However, after these bombings, people were crying 'enough! It must stop!' ... 'Peace! Peace!' But there is no Peace!

"The country got through the bombings, holding its breath. Terrorism is a sick mentality, but it is also a very calculated warfare. It is designed to terrorize, to demoralize, to create division, to wear down, but not to enrage your enemy into full-blown retaliation. They discontinue the bombings for a while and only after life gets back to normal and the rage has been blunted, will the bombings start again.

"This is a peculiar kind of war, this terrorism. It is no sportsmanlike joust between armed opponents, but a bizarre shooting gallery. It rips at the very core of all that is human. And, as its protagonists have calculated, it is cutting at the fabric of this society.

"As for us personally, we are looking to the Lord of Hosts, our Shield and our Defender. If He wants us to leave, then He will provide the means for us to do so; and if He wants us to stay, which is what we are feeling, then He will certainly protect us. It is not easy for our girls to understand and deal with all of this. Julia will not ride the busses anymore, and Laura wanted to know why God allowed all of these people who are not saved

to die and go to Hell. These are difficult questions for all of us. We answer as best we can, praying for wisdom and the right words. We are waiting on the Lord. All of Israel is waiting to see if this all means war or not."

Terrorism is a sick mentality, but it is also a very calculated warfare. It is designed to terrorize, to demoralize, to create division, to wear down, but not to enrage your enemy into full-blown retaliation.

Surely Dr. Iatesta's words and message about his experience with the terrorists in Israel was prophetic of what our nation has experienced in the year 2001 as well as what Israel is experiencing in 2002.

Dr. John struggled for several years to get a permanent visa and to get permission set up a chiropractic practice. He was unable to obtain either, and in September 1997 the Iatestas returned to Portland, Oregon. They left their hearts in Jerusalem, as they had grown to love the people they worked with and to whom they ministered.

Iran
Dr. William Martin

Dr. William Martin, a Christian chiropractor of Iranian descent, married Christina, a woman from the southern part of the old Soviet Union.

Dr. William & Christina Martin

The Martins moved to northern Iran in the late 1970s to be near his wife's homeland, and it was in this part of the world, where the Gospel is almost unknown, that Dr. Martin sought to establish a chiropractic practice as well as to witness for Christ. During part of his time in Iran, Dr. William worked at the J. F. Kennedy Rehabilitation Center where Dr. Flora Colby and Dr. Harry Kalsbeek had worked a few years earlier.

> *"It has been a wonderful opportunity...the past two years in Iran. Our children got acquainted with a different culture and people and had opportunity to see a different way of life...During the past year, I had more spiritual activities than professional work. I was among a group of American Christians and some non-Christian Iranians having Bible studies regularly. Unfortunately, after the political upheaval and the revolution in Iran, these activities completely stopped...many of the foreigners, including Americans, left Iran and...those who stayed [find it] difficult to put up with the Islamic rules as you probably have read in the newspapers.*
>
> *"My professional activity has been successful. Although the activities in the J. F. Kennedy Rehabilitation Center have been completely stopped, I was able to carry on with a private practice. During the past 20 months I have had more that 400 adult patients and about 30 children. I have had about 10% charity patients...*
>
> *"I wish the situation were much better than what it is now so that I would able to stay here in Iran for...another year or two. Unfortunately it is not possible because of my children's school,*

which has been closed...and will not be reopened for the next year or two. With...trust in Jesus, I am sure the political problems will be solved soon, and maybe some of these people will... hear and understand the message of our Lord Jesus for their salvation. We all should pray for...this new government in Iran so by the grace of God this country can stand on its own with a better and healthier economy to survive in the world community." (Martin, Tehran, Iran, 1979)

The Martins spent a little over two years in Northern Iran during the U.S. Presidency of Jimmy Carter. During that time over 50 U.S. citizens were held hostage in Iran for over 400 days. This unstable political situation finally forced the Martins to return to the United States. Only the Lord knows the results of the seeds of his Word that were planted in this predominantly Muslim country.

Honduras, Korea

Dr. Phillip Yoo

The C.C.A. Mission Board does not normally send a member to the mission field without at least two years' experience in practice. Dr. Phillip Yoo, however, graduated from National College of Chiropractic in 1997 and immediately wanted to serve the Lord in Honduras with C.C.A. missionary Dr. Bruce Kniegge. After prayer, the board approved his application, and Dr. Yoo set off for what would turn out to be one of the most dangerous experiences of his life.

Dr. Yoo arrived in Honduras and was met at the airport by Dr. Kniegge. They

Dr. Phillip Yoo

loaded the car and started the journey to the Kniegge's home. Shortly after they left the main road, however, bandits ambushed their car and shot Dr. Kniegge in the head. Dr. Yoo administered emergency care to Dr. Kniegge, got him to a hospital, and oversaw his care until he could be evacuated to Houston for surgery. *(Read the complete story in the chapter on Dr. Bruce Kniegge.)*

Not deterred by the terrifyinng experience of his first hours in Honduras, Dr. Yoo stayed for a year and a half to continue Dr. Kniegge's practice and carry on the mission work. During that time he enjoyed excellent results in his practice and had many opportunities to witness for the Lord.

In September 1999 Dr. Yoo was led to set up practice in Seoul, South Korea. He serves as a bi-vocational missionary, supporting himself in his practice while he continues to work with the churches in the area. He also plans to join a mission outreach into North Korea.

Shell, Ecuador
Dr. Kevin Keough

Dr. & Mrs. Kevin Keough and two of their five children left their home near Kansas City, Missouri, for Ecuador in December 1992. Dr. Kevin had made two short mission trips to Ecuador before and felt called to go back on a permanent basis. Rev. Morley Johnson, Senior Field Missionary with the Independent Evangelical Churches of Puyo Province, which comprised over 500 churches, invited the Keoughs to join in his ministry. This ministry was working primarily with the Quichua Indians.

Dr. Kevin Keough

This missionary venture had its problems from the start, and it is difficult to understand what purpose the Lord had in allowing it to get started at all. First, after Dr. Keough sold his well established chiropractic practice in Missouri, the doctor who bought it immediately declared bankruptcy, moved all of the equipment, furniture, and patient records across the street and started another practice. He never paid Dr. Kevin for his practice or equipment. Dr. Keough was left with an empty building and no equipment, yet he tried to retrieve what he could of his patients and practice and start over again.

After selling his restarted practice a second time, the family left for Ecuador and settled into the city of Shell, Ecuador. Shortly thereafter, the director of the mission who had invited them, Rev. Morley Johnson, died of a sudden heart attack.

After that, and probably because of the stress of all that had happened, Dr. and Mrs. Keough developed family problems. She went back to Missouri and filed for divorce. Dr. Keough has remained in

Ecuador and was dropped from C.C.A. support.

Even though this seemed to be a complete failure as far as our missions program, there was a new program established by the C.C.A. to support the Keoughs, which now has continued to be a blessing for many other C.C.A. missionaries. When the Keoughs were raising their support to go to Ecuador, the mission board of the C.C.A. asked the membership if they would accept a $25.00 dues increase to support resident chiropractic missions. They did, and throughout the past ten years thousands of dollars have been used in this manner, and many of our missionaries have received regular support from that fund. Again we can say that "against all odds ... BUT GOD!"

Part III

Christian Missionaries
who were
Doctors of Chiropractic

Mission Organizations

Many members of the Christian Chiropractors Association are heavily involved in their churches, in Bible studies, outreach programs, and para-church organizations. This chapter briefly tells the stories of four members who went on to serve full-time in ministries apart from chiropracatic. It also highlights three Christian ministries in particular which have benefited from the full-time ministry and leadership of Christian chiropractors.

Wycliffe - Mexico
Dr. and Mrs. James Dean

Before Dr. James Dean graduated from Canadian Memorial Chiropractic College in 1946, he realized that the Lord wanted him in full-time Christian service as a missionary. He later studied at Briarcrest Bible Institute, at schools of linguistics at the University of North Dakota and University of Oklahoma, and in jungle camps for Bible translators in Mexico.

Then Dr. and Mrs. Dean went with Wycliffe Bible Translators first to the Aztecs of Mexico, then to the Philippines. In 1956 they were assigned to open a Wycliffe Summer Institute of Linguistics in New Guinea; it has since become one of Wycliffe's biggest fields. From there the Deans went on to establish Summer Institutes of Linguistics for Wycliffe Bible Translators in Indonesia, India, and Nepal.

In 1971 Dr. Dean also made the initial effort at establishing the Wycliffe ministry in Afghanistan. In his semi-retirement years, he returned to Canada as Home Director.

Dr. Dean was not a missionary chiropractor in the same sense as the Thompsons, Dr. Bridgens Johnson, or Dr. Flora Colby, all of whom were serving on mission fields when the Christian Chiropractors Association was organized. He saw his calling primarily as an administrator, and he knew the

Dr. & Mrs. James Dean

opposition that would come if he tried to use his chiropractic education to any great extent on some fields.

> *"To promote chiropractic in a public way that could stir up the ire of the medical profession in this part of the world might jeopardize my chances of having a part in this great Bible translation program." (Dean)*

However, he prized his chiropractic training and used it whenever the Lord opened the doors for him to do so.

> *"Chiropractic is very dear to me, and I plan to continue to use it wherever and whenever I am given opportunity."* (Dean, 2/14/59)

> *"My chiropractic work is constantly in demand here [in New Guinea]. I know of no other manipulator in this country. The Lord has graciously allowed me to help many people, and I am thankful for the training I received at C.M.C.C."*(Dean, 3/31/65)

> *"When the Lord laid the burden of foreign mission work upon my wife and I, I was half-way through C.M.C.C. We determined to finish our course because we knew the Lord had lead us into it, and then we went on ...[to] Bible training, and from there to various schools and universities for linguistic studies. The Lord has wonderfully enabled me to use my professional training with nationals of the various countries I have been in."*

At last report, the Deans have retired to their home in Calgary, Alberta, Canada.

New Tribes Mission - Columbia
Dr. and Mrs. Richard Hess

Dr. Richard and Margie Hess live and work deep in the jungles of the upper Amazon area of Columbia, South America, with New Tribes Mission. Their mission field is the Macu Indians, one of the last tribes in the country untouched by civilization. These primitive people suffer from malaria, malnutrition, and parasites due to lack of cleanliness and modern medicine.

Dr. Rich's primary duties are Bible translation and church planting. He uses his chiropractic training only as a side ministry as he tries to provide basic health care and training. Dr. Rich wrote of an experience he had with a new young mother.

> *"It finally cooled off and was quiet. Smoke from the two little fires that were under her hammock filled the shack, already beginning to leave a yellow film on the fluorescent light. No bugs–that was a blessing. Glancing up, I checked to see if the*

*I.V. was still dripping. It was OK. Reading and meditating on I
Peter, I thought, 'Could this be a form of suffering?' I had hardly
slept for a week and was exhausted. My desk was a mess, the
stubble on my face was getting longer, and everything seemed
two years behind schedule. But truthfully, I wasn't panicking... I
could rest in the Lord and see this situation as from Him–*

*accepting the responsibilities of
caring for a sick woman and child–not
viewing them as a burden or an
interruption of my plans.*

*"Waama was only sixteen and
had just given birth to a little boy.
She was at the point of death when
she arrived here, having pneumonia
and being dehydrated. Her anemia
was so severe that she had also lost
many of her motor skills and her
ability to speak clearly. Her little boy
was also dehydrated and sick with
bronchitis...*

Dr. Richard Hess

*"'It's not so glamorous now,' I said to myself. She screams
in pain, but can't form words...I can't understand. It was a far
cry from doing the discourse analysis of the language. It would
never appear on anybody's 'to do' list. And yet, God gave us the
privilege to care for this mother and child for two months, taking
shifts night and day–working together as a team. Tears turned
to laughter as we thanked God for working a miracle and
preserving their lives.*

*"... God worked in my own life as well. Those early morn-
ing quiet times with Him were unforgettable. He gave strength
and patience. He even gave Margie and me a newborn baby for
two months. He drastically modified our lives and, also what I
believed to be my daily...'job description'...He is God! Am I
willing to be His servant?" (Hess)*

The Hesses work was difficult, and they did not often see measur-
able results. Yet, we have the testimony of a pair of God's precious
servants doing a job for Him where He has called them to serve.

*"It has now been four years...This would usually be consid-
ered time for furlough and an update on all that has happened.*

*"Yes, we have seen the Lord work miraculously in bringing
us here– keeping us here–and sustaining us here. But as far as
numerical results go, we have none. Language study goes on,
but there still is no Bible teaching, no Bible in their language,*

and the Macu are still in darkness, and many have died without the Gospel.

"We think often of what Jesus said, 'My soul is over-whelmed with sorrow to the point of death. Stay here and keep watch.' Our hearts too have been heavy through the years with the death of Margie's dad, learning and dealing with areas in our own lives, guerrilla threats, co-worker situations, separation from family, visa and government difficulties, and Macu deaths.

"But the Lord has been doing another work here too. He has been working these years in hearts–our hearts–in knowing Him better, trusting Him more, and seeing ourselves better. God not only desires that these Macu people know Him, but he also desires that we would be conformed into the image of Christ. Pray that our hearts would always be tender to Him, aware of our own sinfulness, but focused on His love, faithfulness, forgiveness, and grace. (Hess, 1990)

New Tribes Mission - Brazil
Dr. and Mrs. Jerry Wnuk

After graduating from Logan Chiropractic College in St. Louis in 1969, Dr. Jerry Wnuk found the Lord and attended Prairie Bible Institute at Three Hills, Alberta. In 1975 he and his wife Margorie, with their four children, joined New Tribes Mission to serve in Vianopolis, Brazil.

Dr. Jerry is another example of a chiropractor who uses his chiropractic training only as a sideline of his primary vocation and ministry. On the New Tribes Mission station, he serves as vice-principle of the school and director of the base. In addition to his administrative duties overseeing 150 people, Dr. Jerry teaches chemistry, and Marjorie teaches in the grade school for missionary children.

Dr. Wnuk's chiropractic practice was further limited because of lack of equipment; C.C.A. had had no contact with him, and we were unaware of his ministry needs until 1989. However, Dr. Wnuk wrote the following:

"[My] chiropractic training has proven helpful as I have been able to help...fellow missionaries, students and even some of our local townspeople. The local M.D. at the hospital sends people to me who have back or neck problems, when he doesn't know what to do with them."

Child Evangelism Fellowship
and Luis Palau Crusades
Drs. Frederick and Vickie Kraft

After both graduating from chiropractic college, Drs. Frederick and Vickie Kraft set up practice together on Long Island, New York. After a few years, however, they felt called to attend Columbia Bible College in South Carolina and the Child Evangelism Institute. In the fall of 1968 they became Child Evangelism Fellowship city directors in Dallas, Texas. Theirs soon became one of the most successful Child Evangelism ministries in the

Drs. Fred and Vickie Kraft

country, with hundreds of adults receiving training in children's ministries and thousands of children hearing the Gospel of Jesus Christ.

"...We have two weekly teacher training classes with over 175 adults enrolled... and 24 weekly Good News Clubs in which 381 children are enrolled. Fifty-nine [children] have received Christ in these clubs in the last three months. There have been 26 special parties in addition to the Good News Clubs where another 623 children heard the Gospel and 25 professed to receive Christ. In our State Fair ministry, we had 110 volunteers share the Gospel to over 5000 people of which 431 men, women, and children professed to received Christ." (Kraft, 1978)

After several years with Child Evangelism Fellowship, the Krafts also joined the Luis Palau evangelism ministry. (Luis Palau was then known as the "Billy Graham" of Latin America.) Their focus was still on children.

"It is time to bring you up to date with our activities in this transition period from Child Evangelism Fellowship to the Luis Palau Evangelistic Team. The greatest difference for us is the change from our local, personal ministry to such a world wide one. Writing has been taking a large part of our ministry time. So far, we have completed a series of 14 radio message outlines that have been translated into Spanish. These will be broadcast by Luis Palau and will be heard over a large number of radio stations in Mexico and all of Central and South America.

Pray that God will use these programs to encourage adults to reach children and cause many children to come to Christ."

When Luis Palau expanded his ministry into Scotland, Dr. Fred was there to help with the great crusade in that country.

"By now you know that more that 1600 people [enquired] at the Luis Palau Crusade in Scotland. Statistics show that 70% of those who responded were under 20 years of age. It proves again that children and young people are the responsive ones—the hope of the future of Christianity. We need to thank God and pray daily for men like Luis Palau who have the vision of not neglecting children but reaching whole families and 'every creature' for Christ and the church. Vickie and I thank you for your prayers and your gifts, and remember that 'God is not unrighteous' to forget what you do for missionaries."

Drs. Fred and Vicki participated in Luis Palau Crusades in several cities around the world until 1983 when they left to concentrate on their next calling. All the time they served with Luis Palau, Dr. Fred also maintained leadership of the Child Evangelism ministry in Dallas until 1984.

During this time Dr. Vickie received a Master of Arts Degree in Biblical Studies from Dallas Theological Seminary and began a ministry to women in churches. She served as Minister to Women on the staff of Northwest Bible Church in Dallas. As her ministry grew, Dr. Vickie traveled all over the nation and also overseas leading seminars for women, and Dr. Fred became her business manager. Her ministry organization, called "Titus 2:4 Ministries, Inc" sought to help women realize their God-given gifts and potential in their homes and in the church. Dr. Vickie has now written several books and study guides for her ministry and has appeared on Dr. James Dobson's *Focus on the Family* program.

On December 10, 1997, Dr. Fred passed away of a sudden massive heart attack. Dr. Vickie has carried on her ministry, although her health has been failing in recent years as well. This Christian ministry couple is yet another example of chiropractors serving the Lord in ministry beyond their chiropractic training.

Child Evangelism Fellowship

Rev. J. Irvin Overholtzer started Child Evangelism Fellowship in 1936 in Kansas. One of Rev. Overholtzer's first workers and supporters was a chiropractor, Dr. Frank Mann. Dr. Mann, a graduate of the Minnesota Chiropractic College in 1937, served as executive director of the Child Evangelism Fellowship for the state of Kansas from 1937 till 1942. In 1956 he moved to North Carolina and became state C.E.F. director as well as regional director for the Southeastern United States. In 1958 Dr. Mann became United States National Director for Child Evangelism Fellowship, and soon after that he assumed the duties of International Director. Although he retired from that office in 1971, he continued to travel and speak for the organization for another nine years!

Dr. Frank Mann

Dr. Mann was a humble man with a sincere desire to win children to the Lord Jesus Christ. When he began his ministry with C.E.F. in Kansas, he continued his chiropractic practice, but as he spent more and more time in the organization, he eventually gave up his practice. Under his leadership, the C.E.F. ministry expanded into almost 100 countries around the world and almost every community around North America. Dr. Frank Mann died on October 26, 1983.

Other chiropractors also served in leadership positions in Child Evangelism Fellowship, most notably, Drs. Fred and Vicki Kraft served as C.E.F. directors in Dallas, Texas; Dr. Nadim Nasrallah served as St. Louis area director; Dr. John Felker served as South Carolina state director; and Dr. Glenn M. Hultgren served on the International Board of Trustees from 1968 until 1986.

Awana Youth Ministry

Awana is a program similar to Boy Scouts and Girl Scouts, but it is run by the church and in the church with a strong Christian emphasis. The Canadian director of the Awana program during the late 1970s and early 1980s was a chiropractor from Fonthill, Ontario, Canada, Dr. Ronald Payson. This program, which was well established in the United States, was beginning in Canada when Dr. Payson joined this ministry. It was Dr. Ron who had the burden to see the program expanded into Western Canada from its base in Ontario.

Chinese Nationals Evangelism Commission

The Chinese Nationals Evangelism Commission was formed in 1943 as the dream of another chiropractor, Dr. N. A. Jepson of Seattle, Washington. This mission purposed to support national Chinese pastors and missionaries to help them reach their own people with the Gospel. During the years before the Communists took over China, from 1943 until 1949, the C.N.E.C. had 129 missionaries in China and opened two Bible colleges.

After 1949 the C.N.E.C. centered its work in Hong Kong with an outreach to Chinese people in all of South East Asia. It is still providing support to national Chinese missionaries to Chinese people all over Asia. Dr. Jepson's vision has grown into a most effective indigenous ministry.

Student Projects

One of the original objectives set down in our By-Laws, was to bring Christian students to America and sponsor them through chiropractic College. Our hope and intent was that they would return to their homeland as Doctors of Chiropractic and christian missionaries as well. We were not prepared for a lifetime of support, which many of these would need. Also we still faced the problem of mission societies that refused to include them in their program because of their Chiropractic profession. For this reason this objective was never realized as we had dreamed.

In the very beginning years of the Christian Chiropractors Association, Dr. R. N. Thompson referred two young Ethiopian men to the Association as candidates for chiropractic college. It was his dream that these men might come back to Ethiopia and carry on his work after he left.

In 1957 Mulattu Baffa and Beyenne Mulattu came to Palmer School of Chiropractic in Davenport, Iowa and enrolled as students. They graduated in October 1960 and returned to their native land of Ethiopia. They went on to lead extremely successful lives as missionary chiropractors. Their story is in another chapter in this book.

With the success of this first foreign student project and with the vision of doing this in many other countries around the world, the Association welcomed christian students from many other countries. Most of these students were referred to us by resident missionaries. Students came to America to study Chiropractic from Uruguay, Argentina, Bolivia, Japan, Korea and Ukraine. They started chiropractic college but did not finish. Students came from Lebanon and Ghana and graduated from chiropractic college but could not return to their homeland so have stayed in the U.S. Others from Kenya and Hong Kong came to this Country, graduated from chiropractic college, and went back, but are in commercial practices doing only limited christian service. All of these received the support of the C.C.A. in one way or another.

The success of the first student project was a tremendous encouragement but for one reason or another, it was the only one that worked out as our Association intended.

Hong Kong

Dr. Ted Ong

Ted Ong was born in Amoy, Fuchein on mainland China. He was raised in Hong Kong and graduated from Bethel Seminary in 1958 in

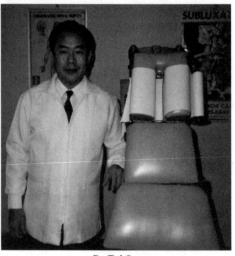

Hong Kong. He went to the Philippines as a missionary to Chinese people in that land. In 1959 he went on staff with the Chinese United Evangelical Church of Manila, Philippines. He served as a translator for Rev. Stanley Yu, a great Chinese Theologian, Evangelist and Bible Teacher and friend of the Christian Chiropractors Association. Rev. Yu was very impressed with Ted and recom-

Dr. Ted Ong

mended that the C.C.A. bring him to the U.S.A. and sponsor him through chiropractic college so that he might be a missionary chiropractor to the Chinese people in Asia. Dr. Carl Cleveland, Sr. granted Ted Ong a full tuition scholarship and Dr. Ted Ong graduated from Cleveland College of Chiropractic in Los Angeles in 1964 and returned to Hong Kong.

It was Ted's desire to return to the Philippines as a missionary chiropractor to continue the mission work which he had been doing before going into chiropractic college. He had his citizenship in Hong Kong and so had to return to the Philippines every few years to renew his visa. He even had to return while he was a student in Los Angeles. But in 1967, the Philippines refused to renew his visa again when he returned from his home in Hong Kong. In doing some investigating, he found out by talking to an old man who had been a chiropractor educated in the U.S. in the early 1920's, that there was a very bad situation that had developed. According to the story, which this old chiropractor told, about 10 chiropractors from the U.S. came to the Philippines in 1922 and 1923 and they started to practice and also they opened up a chiropractic school. At the same time several other national manipulators opened up schools, calling them chiropractic schools and handing out D.C. degrees without proper education or official recognition.

The government stepped in on behalf of the medical profession and passed a law forbidding the practice of Chiropractic in the Philippines, a law which was still in effect at that time (1967). Therefore as a Chiropractor, Dr. Ted was refused a visa for the Philippines. Never-the-less, Ted wrote,

> *"I gave adjustments to my friends and patients for one month in the Philippines. We had about 100 patients altogether there, 15 of them come from the high offices of the Chinese Embassy in Manila. They got good results and many were completely well, which made them think about Chiropractic."*

Although the C.C.A. provided his office in Hong Kong with the necessary equipment for a chiropractic clinic, Dr. Ted had a very hard time getting things working for him. Dr. Ong's ministry consisted of free chiropractic care for missionaries and some of the poor people of Hong Kong. Those who could pay were charged for his services. He did travel into outlining areas of the province setting up clinics and witnessing for the Lord as he had opportunity. He did what mission outreach he could, but without a mission sponsor, he found that he needed almost full time in his practice to support himself and his family. Therefore, his mission work did not advance as much as all of us had hoped.

Dr. Ted was married to Wai Tin, a girl he met in his Chinese Church and they have two children.

Lebanon
Dr. Nadim Nasrallah

On April 23rd, 1966, Nadim Nasrallah from Beirut, Lebanon came to the United States to begin chiropractic college in preparation for serving as a missionary Chiropractor in his home land of Lebanon. Nadim was a Christian convert who had become acquainted with Dr. Flora Colby during her time in Beirut. She highly recommended him to the Christian Chiropractors Association as a prospective student. He came to St.

Dr. & Mrs. Nadim Nasrallah

Louis, Missouri to study at the Logan College of Chiropractic where he graduated in 1969.

During his time as a student at Logan, Nadim got very involved in a Baptist Church, which he joined and was immediately put to work, speaking, and teaching young people. He was called upon to speak at Bible camp and regularly lead the young peoples group. He also was involved in witnessing at the college and leading a small christian group.

Following his graduation from Logan, he attended the Child Evangelism Fellowship Institute and worked as Director of the ministry of C.E.F. in St. Louis for two years. During that time he also attended the Baptist Bible College in Springfield, Missouri, where he met his future wife to be. She was the daughter of a Baptist pastor and had dedicated her life to missionary service.

On April 8th, 1972, Dr. and Mrs. Nadim Nasrallah departed the U.S. for service as missionaries in Lebanon. The C.C.A. had provided his education and several items of equipment necessary for establishing a Christian Missionary Outreach Center in Lebanon. However, shortly after their arrival, civil war broke out and the Nasrallahs had to be evacuated, leaving everything behind.

They returned to St. Louis, hoping the situation in Lebanon would return to some degree of normal, which it never did. Dr. Nasrallah still practices as a Doctor of Chiropractic in the St. Louis area.

Kenya
Dr. George Josiah

Dr. George Josiah graduated from National College of Chiropractic in 1977. George was a native of Kenya and came to the U.S. to study at Fordham University in New York. While there he contacted the Christian Chiropractors Association asking for support to go to chiropractic college. National College had agreed to give him a scholarship and the C.C.A. picked up his living expenses and sponsored him through his college. After graduation, the C.C.A. also sponsored him at the Child Evangelism Fellowship Institute.

Dr. George Josiah

Dr. George then returned to his wife and three children in Kenya.

The C.C.A. provided some professional equipment, a car and financial help for several years in getting started but Dr. George was never able to affiliate with a Mission group to use his Chiropractic with the Mission outreach. At one time, Dr. George wrote:

"High overhead and government regulations pertaining to the establishment of a clinic has me bogged down. Kenicho is the most suitable location for a home/office and avoid commercial zones. It is a small town 200 kilometers from Nairobi. I have taken a teaching job and my salary from it allows me to rent a one-bedroom house. I request very sincerely for you to assist me for one year until I can pick myself up. As it is, you are my only hope!"

George later moved closer to Nairobi when he got his professional registration. In 1980, George wrote,

"I am overflowing with happiness and joy because I just installed the Zenith Adjusting Table (which you sent to me) into what will be my adjusting room. The ship docked in Mombasa on the 17th of April. Documentation and getting custom officials to declare it tax free took me two days and on the 29th of April I got it transported by road to my house.

"It is all smiles and cheers in my house. Oh, it is beautiful! We all knelt down in prayer thanking God and all of you friends that made it possible. We are all looking forward to the great work this table is going to do and with the help of Almighty God we will both perform well.

"Once again thank you all and may God bless you for ever and ever. Thank you brothers and sisters." Dr. George Josiah, Nairobi, Kenya

Dr. George later established his office in Nairobi and lived about 60 kilometers out where he served as a teacher and doctor in a School with over 800 students. Rose Josiah wrote,

"The Masi people are still uncivilized but they are a wonderful people, very warm and friendly. We are starting a Bible class here at the school and George is planning to do some volunteer work at the school for the physically handicapped. There is going to be quite a bit of traveling for both of us. But the Masi tribe is the most forgotten tribe in our country. So we feel that the need for Christians is critical here. We are living practically in the wilderness but we are happy here."

In 1982, the Josiah family moved into Nairobi and rented a three bedroom home. One bedroom was used for Dr. George's chiropractic office. At the same time they continued to develop an outreach for the gospel in their neighborhood. Later he rented a downtown office and shared it with some other doctors. He continued to keep a portable table at this home and maintained a practice there for the poor people. Both Dr. George and Rose maintained contact with the tribal people with whom they had lived and continued Bible studies and ministry with them.

In 1984 Dr. George wrote,

"My work has been rewarding in many ways. Most of my time has been spent in educating my people about chiropractic care. I have appeared twice on national television and once on the national radio network. I have given a number of lectures. The result has been very positive.

"My difficulties have been few, but serious. For one the government of Kenya has a rather negative attitude towards chiropractic. Secondly the health insurance companies in Kenya have refused to pay for chiropractic care. My other constant problem is to secure an office which I can afford. Office space in Nairobi is rather costly. As my wife, Rose, works we have been able to feed ourselves but paying rent for both our house and an office has been a bit of a problem. My goal is to have a place where I can live and practice together.

"Chiropractic has been well received by the people of Kenya, despite the negative attitude of the government. Most of the patients have come to me after medical doctors have failed. In 90% of the cases I have been quite successful in relieving their pain. They have sought me out from all corners of this land. I have been able to witness to my patients as well. My being a Christian has helped me gain the confidence of most of my patients. Although there are hurdles all over the place, there is always the smile of a patient as they say, 'Thank you, Doc!' It is like a miracle. One patient declared to her husband that the moment I touched her all of her pain was gone. So I thank God."

In 1987 Dr. George wrote,

"I have been in the foreign missionary service for over eight years now. I am involved in evangelistic work, which takes me into all parts of the Country. At the same time I introduce chiropractic wherever I go. In my residential estate, we carry out door to door ministry and winning souls to Christ. We are a team of five christians. We meet every Tuesday of the week and at least visit three homes. I also visit churches outside Nairobi at the invitation of the pastor and minister to them by sharing my testimony. I also introduce to the congregation, chiropractic care."

Financial support for Dr. Josiah and his family has been a big concern. The C.C.A. continued supporting them for several years but with all of the other projects, we could not continue. Since that time, the ministry that the Josiah's have been doing has suffered as more and more time has had to be given to making a living. The Josiah's are in our prayers for their safety and for their ministry.

Ghana
Dr. James Frempong

Dr. James Frempong, a native of Accra, Ghana, West Africa, was sponsored by the Christian Chiropractors Association, as a student at the Palmer College of Chiropractic in Davenport, Iowa. He graduated in 1978. Dr. James had a wife and young son with him but left four other children in Ghana when he came to the U.S. In his heart he was dedicated to be a christian missionary chiropractor in Ghana but he had tremendous obstacles to overcome.

In December 1979, Dr. Frempong wrote:

"By the Grace of God, my son and I arrived home in Ghana on Monday, October, 1979. My wife stayed back in the U.S.A. to better herself and finish her education.

"I write this short note to express our thanks and appreciation for making it possible for me to return to Ghana as a missionary Chiropractor. It was quite a joy to reunite with my children. No words can describe the glow of joy that shone in the eyes of the children who have not seen us for almost ten years now.

"We need your prayers now more than ever. I spent all the money I saved before I left the U.S. But the Lord was able to provide our needs as He has always done. We have tremendous work to do in Ghana. With your prayers and financial support, many souls will be touched by the moving of His Spirit. The Lord knows what He is doing through the C.C.A.

"There are a lot of chiropractic cases here in Ghana but

there are tremendous odds against its effectiveness. Malnutrition is an epidemic in this country. Every patient has a vitamin deficiency. Jaundice and stomach problems are slaughtering the population. With proper counseling coupled with spiritual counseling, God's power will be witnessed by many people here in Ghana. The economic woes of Ghana are beyond description. Basic items like soap, toothpaste, razorblades, electric light bulbs, etc. cannot be found anywhere in Ghana. Local hospitals have no supplies. Electricity is in abundant supply, yet surgeons are operating on patients in rooms lit with lanterns. People are sleeping in the streets. Thank God for the warm weather. It was 74 degrees when we arrived. To think of establishing an office is like daydreaming. I have been offered land to build a clinic on but I cannot get the building material even if I had the money to buy it. The Ghanian economic situation is just horrible. You will be kept posted of every progress. Yours in the service of Christ, James Frempong, D.C."

The C.C.A. raised the money and sent chiropractic adjusting tables and other equipment to Ghana for Dr. Frempong. Shortly after his arrival in Ghana, Dr. James had a series of misfortunes: his mother-in-law died unexpectedly and his wife Sophie was in the U.S. and not able to return. Five days after that funeral, James' brother died. Then Dr. Jim was bitten by a poisonous snake and nearly died. Then his youngest son, Derek, became extremely ill with a fever. After that, political upheaval caused tremendous delay in communication and it was impossible for Sophie in America to know what was happening and how her family was doing in Ghana.

Dr. Frempong tried several times to get established in Ghana, but for political and economic reasons he was never able to get established there. In 1981 he returned with his wife and family to Davenport, Iowa.

Stillwagon, Hultgren, and Kalsbeek
The World Tour of Missions

At the 1967 Christian Chiropractors Association convention in Dearborn, Michigan, the board of directors decided to send representatives to do a worldwide survey of missions. The purpose of the trip was three-fold:

1. Visit as many of the missionary chiropractors on the field as possible; determine what if any help they need which we might be able to supply.
2. Determine which mission societies would welcome a chiropractor to serve with them on the mission field.
3. Assess areas of the world where missionary chiropractors might find a fruitful field of service. Especially investigate how receptive the local population in third world countries might be to chiropractic care. Many of these countries have no license requirements and thus no legal restrictions.

After prayerful consideration, C.C.A. President Dr. Glenn Stillwagon of Monongahela, Pennsylvania, Missions Committee Chairman Dr. Harry Kalsbeek of Castro Valley, California, and I (Executive Secretary Dr. Glenn Hultgren of Fort Collins, Colorado) were chosen to go.

Planning the route took some time, but we finally decided to go through Mexico and Central America, then to South America and across the South Atlantic to Africa. After crossing Africa, we would go the Middle East and then to India, Vietnam, Hong Kong, the Philippines, Taiwan, Japan, Hawaii, and home. At the very least, this would take about two months' time. At the last minute, Dr. Kalsbeek found he could not leave his office for that length of time and decided instead to join Dr. Stillwagon and I in Greece for the Middle Eastern and Asian part of the tour.

On January 14, 1968, Dr. Stillwagon left from Pittsburgh and I from Denver; we met in the airport in Mexico City. We both found it hard to leave our wives and children, who were small at that time. He had four boys ages four to ten and I had two girls, age two and eleven and two boys, ages five and eight. We knew we left a huge responsibility on our wives, but we also knew that the Lord was in this venture, and He gave us peace. We had to commit our families to the Lord and trust Him to care and provide for them in our absence. The following is taken from daily diaries that Dr. Stillwagon and I kept during the trip.

Mexico

We arrived at the Reforma International Hotel in Mexico City, had a real Mexican meal, (too spicy for Glenn S.), a time of prayer for the adventure we are about to embark upon, and went to bed. The next morning we learned the difficulties of not knowing the local language. We hailed a cab to the airport and soon wished to express our displeasure at the extremely fast, reckless drive. Our driver, however, did not understand English. At the airport, we could not read the signs and could not understand the announcements; we almost ended up on a plane for Havana instead of Oaxaco. (In Spanish, *Oaxaco* is pronounced *wa-haw-ka*.)

Dr. Lester Blank, the first missionary chiropractor we hoped to visit, was serving the Lord in the mountains northwest of Oaxaco. We had arranged for him to meet us at the airport, but when we arrived, he was not there. Again, we were frustrated by the language barrier. We were in a place very strange to us and had no way to find out what to do. Finally, about 1-1/2 hours later, Dr. Blank arrived. The transmission on his VW bus had gone out. He had hailed a taxi to the airport, but we would have to rent a car to drive back into the mountains. Unfortunately, it was now siesta time, and all businesses were closed until 4:00 p.m. We did not know at the time that the Lord was preparing us for situations we would be facing in the weeks ahead.

After siesta time, we were able to rent a VW bug. It got dark before we got very far, and driving on narrow dirt roads through obscure Indian villages in the Central Highlands of Mexico was yet another way of preparing us for the rest of the trip. Five hours later we arrived at Laguna where the Blanks live and work. It was about 150 miles from Oaxaco and 300 miles south of Mexico City. MaryLou Blank had a tasty meal waiting, and we were very hungry as we had had nothing to eat since leaving Mexico City.

The Blank's home was a hand-hewn log cabin with a loft, and as they had six children, it was very cozy. Their hospitality was unforgettable, and as little as they had, they shared willingly with us. Of course there was no electricity or running water, and neither Glenn S. nor I had ever shaved with a razor blade–lots of blood the first morning.

We treated a few patients at the Blank's home the next morning, including a 9-month-old baby with a high fever and diarrhea and a man with a machete wound to the scalp. The man had just placed a large flap of his scalp back into place and put his cap on tightly to hold it there. It had been several days, and the skin had grown on twisted with infection under the flap. We didn't think an adjustment would help him very much, so we made arrangements to transport him to a medical doctor in town.

We made a house call–traveling four hours by VW and hiking the last mile. The man was dying of tuberculosis. He lay on a dirty mat on the ground in his four-foot high "house." The inside was covered with pitch from a constantly burning fire.

The man's wife was eating a spaghetti squash with her fingers. She reached into a pile of corncobs for a couple of dirty, broken gourds. Dumping the dirt out of the gourds, she put some of her squash in them and handed one to Dr. S. He asked Dr. Blank in English, "Do I have to eat this stuff?" Dr. Blank, the seasoned missionary, took that opportunity to teach us novices a lesson: "If you want to be 100% with these people, you will." And so we did. Many times throughout our trip we faced similar situations and remembered Dr. Blank's words.

That evening the Blanks invited the Indians for a slide program with a gospel message. The Indians seemed to have accepted the Blanks both for their health care and the missionary message. The years to come should prove to be a harvest time for the church in this area.

On Wednesday, January 17, we returned to Oaxaco, spent the night there, and caught a plane the next day for Mexico City. From there we flew to Panama City where we spent the next night. We were impressed with what we saw of Panama and were sorry we could not spend more time there.

Ecuador

On Friday, January 19, we caught an early Ecuadorian Airlines flight from Panama City and arrived in Quito, Ecuador, at 7:30 a.m. "Uncle Joe" Christopher and Mrs. Dave Landers, from HCJB Radio, were there to meet us. I stayed with the Landers, and Dr. S. stayed with Albert and Lorna Enns. We toured the HCJB Radio headquarters and transmission station, as well as the Alliance Academy, a school for missionary children, and the Wycliffe Bible Translators base station. We set up a chiropractic clinic each day we were there and adjusted dozens of missionaries from all of these groups.

One highlight was a dinner in the home of Abe and Marge Van DerPuy. Abe was the director of HCJB at that time. His first wife had died of cancer, leaving him with three children. Marge was the widow of Nate Saint who was killed by the Auca Indians some 12 years earlier. She, too, had been left with three children. Sitting around the table that night were six of the finest teenagers we had ever met—the blended family of the Saints and the Van DerPuys.

Two of the Saint's children had been baptized by the very Auca Indians who had killed their father but had since become Christians. Another missionary who had been killed with Nate Saint in 1956 was Jim Elliott whose brother and mother were chiropractors. His brother later became President of Western States Chiropractic College in Portland, Oregon. (The group of martyrs also included Pete Fleming, Roger Youderian and Ed McCulley) The killing of these five missionaries 12 years before was still fresh on the minds of all of the missionaries in Ecuador.

Another highlight of the visit to Quito was the Sunday morning service at the English Fellowship Baptist Church. Pastor Bob Savage, from Jackson, Michigan, had 160 missionaries in his congregation. His message that morning was "Getting along with Other Christians." Both Dr. S. and I had great discussions with our missionary hosts about their concerns, frustrations, problems as well as their goals in service. What a wonderful group of missionaries we met in Quito!

Peru

On Monday, January 22, we flew from Ecuador to Lima, Peru. We hoped to visit Dr. Larry Garman and his wife Addie and family in the northeastern part of Peru, on the headwaters of the Amazon. This proved to be impossible as planes were not flying over the mountains, and it would take three days in and three days out to go by land and river to reach the Garmans. We also had hoped to visit the Wycliffe base at Yreno Cocha but bad weather prevented that trip also.

We stayed at the Wycliffe home in Lima, visited their downtown office in the Department of Education building, and visited with many Wycliffe missionaries including Bob Vance, assistant Director for Wycliffe. We also visited with missionaries from many different mission societies including Hazel McCrary of Child Evangelism Fellowship, Melvin Hodges and Walter Erickson of the Assembly of God Bible Institute, and Hal Coconower of the Latin American Mission.

Bolivia

On January 24 we left Peru on Bolivian Airlines for Cochabamba, Bolivia, after a brief stop at the highest airport in the world, LaPaz, Bolivia. In Cochabamba, Dr. J. Bridgens Johnson drove us to meet his excited wife Dorothy who was waiting to greet us at their home. *(More about Dr. Bridge and Dorothy Johnson in the Operation Bolivia chapter.)* After lunch and a tour of their two-story home/clinic/ church building, barely had time for a rest before Dorothy had prepared a tremendous dinner for us and a missionary couple from Scotland, Mr. & Mrs. Sam and Jessie Landers of the Plymouth Brethern Church.

The next day we began to experience Cochabamba. Our first stop was a "hospital," which was hardly even a clinic, to see a missionary friend of the Johnsons, Miss Sarah Zurita. Miss Zurita was diagnosed with "leukemia." She had suffered uncontrolled nosebleeds for over a week and her nose was packed. I gave her an adjustment and promised to see her again the next day.

After dinner we attended a prayer meeting with about 40 Bolivians packed into a small hut with mud walls, a dirt floor, and a 25-watt light bulb in the middle of the room. Dr. Bridge translated as Dr. S. told of our mission and I shared from Scripture. It was a great day, and we slept well that night.

On Friday after a big breakfast with the Johnsons, we returned to the hospital to see Sarah. She was doing much better, and her nose had stopped bleeding. As I gave her another adjustment, we could not help noticing how filthy everything was. Laundry was hanging on the balcony railing, and Sarah's bed had not been changed for several days and had dry blood all over it.

After touring the city and visiting with many of Dr. Bridge's friends and fellow missionaries, we returned to the clinic and took care of more of his patients. After dinner we again went out to a village church much like the one the night before.

On Saturday we filmed an interview with the Johnsons and then returned to the hospital to see Sarah. She was so improved that she was ready to be discharged. We continued to take care of many patients in the clinic as well as acquaint ourselves with many different mission organizations and their various ministries. A visit to the Bolivian farmer's open market was an indescribable experience which gave us a much deeper understanding of Bolivian culture.

On Sunday we had Sunday school and church in a packed chapel at the Johnson home. The Bolivian Christians sang at the top of their voices in praise to the Lord and both Dr. S. and I shared from the Word. They closed by singing all five verses of "God Be With You Till We meet Again," in Spanish. (I never knew it had five verses!) Thus we bid farewell to the wonderful Bolivian Christians at the Open Door Church of Bolivia.

We left Cochabamba on Monday morning on a flight for Buenos Aires with a 15-minute stop (more or less) in Santa Cruz, Bolivia. Missionary Carl Walters of the Gospel World Mission met us. This flight from Cochabamba to Buenos Aires was a once-a-week flight; if we missed our plane, our entire trip around the world would be thrown off schedule.

Rev. Walters took us for a tour of the town, then to his home. We gave adjustments to several missionaries, had tea and cookies, and toured the town some more. We were sure we had missed our plane, but true to Bolivian schedule, we arrived at the airport in plenty of time; in fact, we still had to wait before the plane left.

The plane was an old DC-7 that took over five hours of rough flying to get from Santa Cruz to Buenos Aires. Alberto Pardo, our flight attendant, was a member of the Open Door Church in Cochabamba. We had met him the day before. When we arrived in Buenos Aires, we found out he was also the mechanic who checked out the plane for its return flight to Bolivia.

Argentina

A missionary friend of mine, Miss Theda Krieger, met us in Buenos Aires. Miss Theda was a Child Evangelism Fellowship missionary whom we had entertained in our home in the States. She is also the one who led Luis Palau to the Lord in a Good News Club years before. Rev. Palau went on to become the greatest evangelist in Latin America and was called the Spanish Billy Graham. It was a thrill to meet Theda again and also to meet her parents, missionaries from Germany, then in their 90s and blind. We all went out for a great Argentine steak dinner and didn't get to bed until 2:00 a.m. We had visited with 117 missionaries in South America.

Ghana

Our flight across the South Atlantic on Swiss Air was in a beautiful plane with excellent service. After a brief stop in Rio de Janeiro, we arrived in Dakar, Senegal, after 11:00 p.m. local time. Our next flight was to leave at 5:30 a.m., so we stayed in the airport. The lights were turned out, and we were the only ones around. We tried to sleep and write letters. Around 3:00 a.m. a couple of French men came in. They had gone to the hotel but found it so bad that they returned to the airport instead of staying there the rest of the night. We thanked God for keeping us in the airport.

The plane was late, we were tired, and Glenn S. had a bad case of diarrhea. The trip from there to Monrovia, Liberia, and on to Accra, Ghana, was not a pleasant one. In Accra we were to catch an Ethiopian Airlines flight to Addis Ababa. When we arrived, however, we discovered that the plane had not been flying for several months, and the International travel agents did not know about it. We were stranded in Accra.

We booked a room in the International Hotel and visited the beach just a short distance from the hotel. We were unable to reach any of the missionaries we tried to call. Then, while walking through the lobby of the hotel, someone yelled out, "Where you guys from?" Obviously an American! Thomas Oduro-Kwartin was a Ghanese who had spent a number of years in Chicago, and he offered to chauffeur us in his brand new Chevrolet convertible. He drove us to a Mennonite Mission we had heard of a short distance out of town.

We enjoyed a very interesting visit with two missionary nurses. Then while exploring, we stumbled into a pagan animistic worship area with altars, idols, and all kinds of witchcraft items. When we returned, the missionaries were horrified that we had gone there, but we got some great pictures and a real experience with native African religion. Tom also showed us the University of Ghana, the American Embassy, and other sites around town. We met six missionaries while in Ghana.

The next day Tom got us on a plane for Nairobi, Kenya, with a stop over in Lagos, Nigeria. A civil war was going on in Nigeria, and the airport was under siege. We did not stay long. After a brief stop in Entebbe, Uganda, we arrived in Nairobi late at night.

We had not planned to visit Kenya, so we were without a visa. We obtained an overnight visa that allowed us to go to the Ambassador Hotel for the night. In the morning we caught an Ethiopian Airlines flight for Addis Ababa. We would have liked to stay in Entebbe and Nairobi longer as both seemed very pleasant with much to offer tourists.

We, however, were not tourists–we were on a mission, and personal desires had to be put aside.

Ethiopia

Our Ethiopian chiropractors, Dr. Mulattu Baffa and Dr. Beyenne Mulatu met us at the Addis Ababa airport. We also saw an unusual number of armed soldiers, a red carpet on the walkway, and a couple of brand new Cadillacs. We thought they had gone overboard in their welcome, but soon discovered that Marshall Tito from Yugoslavia had arrived at the airport at about the same time, and His Majesty Haille Sellassie was there to meet him. Security was all show and not very tight. We took pictures of both of them.

From the airport Dr. Stillwagon went with Mulu and Beyenne to Sheshemane, Ethiopia, and I went to Dembi Dollo, Ethiopia. Before leaving for Dembi Dollo, I spent the night at the Sudan Interior Mission Home in Addis and had a great time of fellowship with several missionaries. Of course most of them needed adjustments. I returned to my room rather late at night and found that a Mission Aviation Fellowship pilot from Kenya had been given the other bed in my room.

When I told him I was a chiropractor, he said, "I'm not supposed to be here because M.A.F. does not normally fly into Ethiopia. When I came in this morning, I injured my back unloading the plane. Isn't that just like the Lord to provide a chiropractor in the middle of Africa, in a place where I am not supposed to be, just after I injured myself?" I gave him an adjustment on the floor. The next day he was fine and flew back to Kenya.

On Sunday morning I caught a C-47 airplane for Dembi Dollo where my brother Kert Hultgren and his family were serving as missionaries with the Presbyterian mission. Dembi Dollo is at the far western side of Ethiopia, not far from Sudan. There were no roads into the village, and the only vehicle in town was a four-wheel drive Land Rover owned by the mission. The mission had established a school, a hospital, and a church, all of which were doing very well. On Monday morning, I visited the hospital and adjusted the newborn baby and then to the school where Kert was teaching.

Due to the cancellation of our flight out of Ghana, I was able to spend only one day there, but it was a great mission experience as well as a great time with my brother and his family. After lunch I caught a plane back to Addis Ababa. After supper at the Sudan Interior

Mission House, I left for Shashemane with Yohannes, one of Dr. Thompson's trusted workers. The trip was a four-hour drive through the rain on primitive roads at speeds up to 90 miles per hour. But Yohannes knew the road as he was the highway's engineer.

Sheshemane was where Dr. Robert N. Thompson had established the S.I.M. Southern Leper Colony years before. The mission staff now consisted of three M.D.s and four nurses. Dr. Mulu was one of the doctors on the mission team; his job was to triage the new patients and recommend the type of care they were to receive. He also had charge of 15 clinic stations in the countryside away from the leprosarium. The leprosarium housed 700 leper patients. The outstations were serving another 16,000 to 17,000 patients. They also had a clinic for non-leper patients.

We visited the entire compound, observed the hospital work, traveled to a couple of out land clinics, and of course discussed much with the missionaries. We were shocked by the advanced level of disease. Patients do not come to the clinic until all tribal customs have failed. We were disappointed at how little chiropractic was being used, but we also realized that most of these cases were so far advanced that surgery and palliative care was the main concern. Finally, we both had the privilege of speaking in the leper church.

The next day, we traveled south to Wando and Della visiting mission stations and seeing the country. I was anxious to see Wando-Emmaus where the Mae Hultgren Memorial Project was established. *(Read the full description of this project in its own section of the book)* The coffee harvest was in full swing, and with 88,000 coffee trees, it was a busy place. Seeing coffee harvested was a new experience. The coffee plantation had made the project a self-supporting outreach mission station, and at that time employed 102 men. Dr. Mulu indicated his desire to move from Sheshemane and eventually establish his clinic, home, and mission station here.

One last footnote: the week before we arrived, a 22 foot python was killed on the plantation. Dr. Mulu gave me the skin, which I sent home. It was a shock for my wife, but a great show-and-tell for my kids.

We left Ethiopia on Saturday, February 10, after a tremendous send-off by all of the missionaries, both in Sheshemane and at the S.I.M. Home in Addis. They were all most appreciative of our visit. In all, we visited 70 missionaries in Ethiopia.

Israel and Lebanon

We were two hours late leaving the airport and were concerned about making our connection in Athens for Tel Aviv. Dr. Harry Kalsbeek was to join us at the airport in Athens for the remainder of the trip. When we arrived, Dr. Harry was standing in the door of the plane telling the crew of our pending arrival and physically keeping the plane from taking off.

We arrived in Tel Aviv Saturday night, rented a car, and drove to Jerusalem where we rented rooms at the YMCA. The next morning we contacted Rev. Alexander Wachtel, a Nazarene missionary who served as our guide around Jerusalem. It had been only eight months since the Israelis took control of East Jerusalem, and there was much military hardware strewn over the highways. From Jerusalem we drove to Nazareth where we met Child Evangelism Fellowship missionary Wayne King. He served as our guide in that part of the country.

We left Israel February 13 after visiting a total of seven missionaries. Our flight landed in Cyprus before heading on to Beruit, Lebanon. We ended up just 75 miles from where we started that morning, but with no direct travel between Israel and Lebanon, the trip took all day.

Rev. Hazel Kleintop and Rev. Abraham Rababy met us at the airport. They are friends and associates of our missionary chiropractor, Dr. Flora Colby. Dr. Flora had served for many years in Lebanon, but at that time was serving in Doha, Qatar. That evening we all spoke in Rev. Kleintop's Pentecostal church.

While in Beruit, we met Nadim Nasrallah's mother. At the time, C.C.A. was supporting Nadim as a student at Logan Chiropractic College in St. Louis, Missouri. We also met Miss Lebibi Shammas, another Child Evangelism Fellowship missionary, who was doing a tremendous ministry throughout the Middle East in countries where no one else could go with the Gospel of Jesus Christ. (I visited a number of Child Evangelism missionaries because at that time, and for many years to come, I served on the International Board of Trustees of Child Evangelism Fellowship.)

Qatar

While in Beruit, we obtained "No Objection Certificates" for our travel into Qatar, and late at night on February 14 we left Beruit for Doha, Qatar. Dr. Colby and some of her friends met us at the airport. We stayed in the large rented house where Dr. Colby had her clinic as well as a chapel.

Doha is 100% Moslem. The only approved Christianity is a one-hour service on Sundays by a Catholic priest who must leave before sunset. The churches we visited, an Indian congregation where a visiting evangelist from Pakistan was preaching and Dr. Colby's chapel, were truly underground churches. Mission activity was definitely "against all odds," but God was working. Each of these churches had good attendance, and we were very impressed with the mission work that Dr. Colby was able to do.

Dr. Flora is highly respected by several influential businessmen. She was invited to Qatar by one of the businessmen, and her practice had done very well until recently. She told of some severe medical opposition in recent months that had affected her practice and her outreach. *(Read the chapter on Dr. Flora Colby for more on her ministry.)*

India

We left Doha, Qatar, at 1:30 a.m. on Saturday, February 17, and arrived in Bombay, India, at 6:30 a.m. that same morning. Since Dr. Stillwagon and I had been in Africa within the last 10 days and had not had yellow fever vaccinations, we were quarantined for three days. This proved to be a blessing as we really needed the rest, and the facility was better than most hotels in India. The director of the facility was a Christian, which in India is very unusual; she brought in a number of people to meet us, pray with us, and share Bible studies.

We ended up ministering to and adjusting almost everyone in the facility, including the director of the facility as well as the health director of the port of Bombay, Dr. Ramamarti, and his assistant, Dr. Saha. They came to ask about our reason for being there and about chiropractic. We gave them adjustments and explained our mission. Both of these doctors then brought their spouses and other members of their family for adjustments.

When we left the facility on Monday to fly from Bombay to New Delhi, Dr. Ramamarti gave us a letter of introduction to the Minister of Health for the Nation of India. We were unable to get an appointment at the Ministry of Health that day, so we rented a taxi and spent the day shopping and sightseeing in Agra and at the Taj Mahal.

Tuesday we met with various department ministers at the Ministry of Health of India. They were warm and friendly, and we ended up demonstrating chiropractic to them by giving adjustments on desks or whatever we could find. Then we got an audience with Dr. P. K. Duraiswamy, the Minister of Health. He was not as warm or friendly as the other ministers had been. When we asked about sending a missionary chiropractor to India, he did not encourage us. Then he told us he was educated as an Orthopedic Surgeon at John Hopkins in the U.S. Once again we saw the long arm of the North American Medical establishment and its prejudice.

Leaving the Ministry of Health, we went to meet Rev. Abner Nelson, an outstanding Indian national who pastored the only evangelical church in Delhi. His testimony was outstanding. Raised as a Hindu, he left his religion to study communism in Moscow. Abner returned to India to help destroy the evangelical church but was converted while attacking a congregation one evening. He then took the name of the American pastor who led him to the Lord and immediately started preaching the Gospel and establishing churches. He was known among the Christians as the Apostle Paul of India due to the numerous times he was beaten and jailed.

Vietnam

Before leaving India, we visited the American Embassy to check on the situation in our next stop–Vietnam. What little news we had heard indicated that the war had really heated up; however, the embassy had no word of caution for us. On Wednesday, February 21, we left New Delhi on Air France for Vietnam with an intermediary stop in Bangkok.

Upon arriving in Bangkok, Dr. Kalsbeek called the Christian and Missionary Alliance office to inquire about our missionary in Vietnam, Dr. John Hall. He learned that Dr. Hall and his family had been evacuated from Dalat, Vietnam, a few days earlier and were in Bangkok. (Read the chapter on Dr. John and Penny Hall for more on their ministry.) We were unable to speak with John or Penny in Bangkok but left word and boarded the plane for Vietnam.

It was soon obvious that this was not the usual flight. We had the entire Boeing 707 to ourselves, and the flight attendant asked if we were going to Vietnam "by choice." When we arrived, the first thing we saw was a huge hole in the roof of the terminal building waiting area. A communist mortar shell had hit there a few days before.

Dr. Harry met some missionaries in the terminal building; they were evacuating to Bangkok. Dr. Stillwagon called a friend, Col. Jim Warren. The colonel took him to Ton Sun Nuit Airbase where he stayed for the night. Dr. Kalsbeek and I went to the Christian and Missionary Alliance mission home.

We learned that we had arrived in Vietnam just two weeks after what was called the "Tet Offensive." The communists had pulled out all the stops to drive the Americans out of Vietnam. Several Wycliffe translators and Christian and Missionary Alliance members were taken captive and six were killed in the Ben Mi Thaut and Dalat areas. We visited with those who knew them. Reggie Reimer had just returned from burying the martyred ones when we arrived, and he showed us pictures and described the massacre scene. Hank and Vange Blood and their three-year-old daughter were among the captives. Hank was later killed, but we got to meet Vange and her daughter in Manila a few days later after they had been released.

We learned that the Halls were involved in translating the Bible into the language of a mountain tribal people. All of the missionaries spoke very highly of them and their work as well as of Dr. Hall's chiropractic work.

Rev. John Peters of the Pocket Testament League drove us around the city of Saigon to see the tremendous war devastation. We met 32 Wycliffe, C&MA, and P.T.L. missionaries in Vietnam; our interviews with them were inspiring. The lives of these missionaries were on the line, and some had died for the cause of Christ. Their wives and many of their colleagues had been evacuated to safer areas.

That night 28 Vietnamese soldiers patrolled our rooftop to protect us as mortar shells flew overhead and bombs burst all around us. Helicopters with huge searchlights circled us all night long. It was an emotional day and half.

Dr. Harry's son Brian was in the Army stationed at Cam Ran Bay. Harry was hoping to get to see Brian, but that was impossible due to the circumstances. They did finally did get to speak by telephone, however, which was quite a thrill for both of them.

Hong Kong

We left for Hong Kong shortly after noon on February 22 where we called our friend and fellow chiropractor, Dr. Ted Ong. We had first heard of Ted when he was working as an interpreter for our evangelist friend, Rev. Stanley Yu, in the Philippines. C.C.A. arranged to sponsor him through Cleveland Chiropractic College in Los Angeles. He graduated in 1966 and returned to his native Hong Kong to set up practice and carry on a mission outreach.

The C.C.A. had given Dr. Ted financial support and chiropractic equipment, but he had found it impossible to support himself and do mission work as well. Therefore, he was in a commercial chiropractic practice in downtown Kowloon, Hong Kong. We tried to help Dr. Ted find a way to increase his mission outreach through his chiropractic, but we could see that he needed a mission society sponsor.

Dr. Ted was a great guide, and we met many missionaries and saw many different ministries, especially those with the Chinese National Evangelistic Crusade, a mission which was organized by a fellow chiropractor in Seattle, Dr. Jeppson.

Philippines

We left Hong Kong late Sunday evening, February 25, for Manila. Miss Happy Minot of Wycliffe met us at the airport and escorted us to the Wycliffe mission home. We spent the next day visiting with missionaries at the Wycliffe home and also at the C&MA headquarters– 18 missionaries in all. We had so many questions, and it seemed so little time to learn all we wanted to know about the their work. We developed a tremendous respect for the Wycliffe translation ministry. We also visited the very impressive United Evangelical Chinese Church in Manila.

On Tuesday, February 27, we got up at 3:00 a.m. to catch a plane to Mindanao for a visit with our good friends, Dick and Betty Elkins who are Wycliffe workers at the Nasuli Base Station in central Mindanao. Our plane landed at Cagayan del Oro and we were met by Paul Carlson and his helio courier operated by Jungle Aviation and Radio Service, a branch of the Wycliffe ministry. The Elkins met us when we arrived at Nasuli. During our stay at Nasuli, Paul was our flight chauffeur as we were escorted to several villages where missionaries were busy translating the Bible into the language of the local people.

We adjusted missionaries during every spare minute. Dick Elkins is an amateur chiropractor who, by trial and error, has developed some manipulative techniques to help many of the missionaries over the years. We gave him some counsel and encouraged him in his work.

On Wednesday Dick Elkins took us to Barandias, the village where he has spent fifteen years translating. We landed on the 800-foot runway carved out of the jungle and walked to his jungle home. Dick and Betty have done an outstanding work. At that time, they had translated a major portion of the New Testament, had a number of converts, established a church, and trained a pastor and lay leadership.

Back in Nasuli on Wednesday evening, we all spoke at the

mid-week prayer and Bible hour with the resident missionaries. These people were so appreciative of us and of our visit. They begged us to find a chiropractor to serve permanently on the base.

On Thursday, February 29, we left Nasuli early in the morning and returned to Manila. On Friday, March 1, Dr. Kalsbeek went on to Tiawan and then to Japan. Dr. Stillwagon and I were exhausted from our trip, and arranged to go directly to Honolulu from Manila. Before leaving, however, Dr. S. and I caught a plane for Baguio in central Luzon to see if we could meet any of the Philippine psychic surgeons.

Once in Baguio, a travel agent and guide, Jerry Montanez, drove us to the village of Carmen. There we met Marcelo Jainar, a"pastor" and resident psychic healer. He let us witness three procedures (done on the altar at the front of the "church"). One was a man with stomach ulcers; the second, a woman with an ovarian problem; and the third, a woman with stomach ulcers. (These are all his diagnoses which we had no way of verifying.) After watching this and filming it, we were uncertain of what we had seen. After thirty years, we still do not know what we saw. It definitely was not Christian according to Biblical healing! But neither is it quackery, sleight of hand, or magic. We felt it was a form of Satanic healing!

On Saturday we returned to the Wycliffe home in Manila and saw Vange Blood and her daughter. The communists had held them hostage the last couple of weeks in Vietnam, and her husband, Hank, had been killed. We visited with her and I adjusted her daughter. Vange said she was uninjured but had a huge cut on her leg. It was a very emotional meeting for us. We met a total of 80 missionaries in the Philippines.

Later that evening we caught a flight for Honolulu where we met our wives and spent a few days in valuable rest and relaxation. It had been seven weeks since we had seen them. So much had happened in that time that we needed time to let it settle in and to try to comprehend what we had done. The Lord had been good; we did not lose anything, and we maintained good health except for occasional stomach upset from some of the different foods we ate.

We had more than accomplished all that we set out to do. Furthermore, we had a far deeper appreciation for and understanding of Christian missionaries in underdeveloped areas. In all, we had met 333 missionaries in 25 countries serving with 35 different mission societies on 75 mission stations. Praise the Lord.

Short-Term Missionary Chiropractors

It was in the January 1963 issue of *The Christian Chiropractor* that the idea of short-term missionaries first came up. At that time it was noted that the Christian Medical Society had sponsored 14 of its members as short-term missionaries. Of course they had the support of *"65 pharmaceutical and surgical supply companies"* and we knew the C.C.A. members would have to pay their own way. Yet we felt that the Lord was in this project and several of our resident missionary chiropractors had asked for some of our members to come to their field and offer them some short-term support. It wasn't until the annual convention of 1971 in Winona Lake, Indiana, that the C.C.A. voted to officially develop its short-term mission program. By that time several of our members had already completed short-term assignments.

Dr. Esther Mork of Janesville, Wisconsin had already gone to Bolivia in 1960 to work with Dr. and Mrs. Bridgens Johnson for a few weeks before the C.C.A. started its short-term missionary program. More about the ministry of Dr. Esther Mork in the chapter on Dr. & Mrs. J. Bridgens Johnson.

Another of the first short-term volunteer missionary chiropractors was **Dr. Ethel Brindle** of Waynesboro, Pennsylvania. Dr. Brindle was one of our older members in semi-retirement, who went to Lebanon to work with Dr. Flora Colby on July 7,1965 and stayed there until October 28, 1965. She traveled from Lebanon to India to work with the Billy Graham Crusade and then to Hong Kong to visit with Dr. Ted Ong. From Hong Kong, Dr. Ethel traveled across the Pacific making a complete around the world trip

In July 1965, **Dr. Stanley Lindblom** of Plentywood, Montana went as a short-term missionary chiropractor to work with Dr. Dinah Van Dyken in Window Rock, Arizona on the Navajo Reservation. His story is in another chapter of the book.

Another short-term missionary chiropractor who should be mentioned because of her unique type of service was that of **Dr. Diane (Davis) Monger.** Dr. Diane married a Captain in the U.S. Air Force shortly after her graduation from Palmer College of Chiropractic in 1966, and they were sent to the Philippines. While stationed at Clark Air Force Base north of Manila, and living off base, Dr. Diane started a practice of taking care of missionaries in the area. She reported that this was a very fruitful and rewarding experience. Her message to the C.C.A. was to recognize this need and to send someone to the Philippines to do this on a permanent basis. She was there for about one year in the late 1960's.

When Dr. Diane returned to the States she lived in Roseburg, Oregon and recorded some songs using her talents in piano, organ, violin, viola and guitar. One week after her record was released, she was injured in an automobile accident and was partially paralyzed, unable to continue her chiropractic practice or play the musical instruments again.

When **Dr. Claire Blossom** of Vassar, Michigan retired after practicing chiropractic for 45 years, he began a short-term mission outreach that turned out to be much more than short-term. Dr. Blossom's wife died in February 1971, at about the same time as his retirement and he dedicated himself to service for his Lord. He went to Haiti, Venezuela, Bonair and finally to Brazil where he stayed for several years, coming "home" only for rest. He would come home for a few weeks and then return to Brazil. He continued this ministry until he was into his eighties.

Dr. Claire Blossom

Dr. Blossom's primary calling was to take care of missionaries and he ably did so in several countries of the Caribbean and South America. One missionary wrote,

> We want to write this letter to you to tell about the visit that Dr. C. E. Blossom made here two times recently in December of 1977 and January 1978 and again in March of 1978. It was a sheer delight to have him stay with us in our home. He was very flexible and pleasant and related well to our two little daughters. The first time he was here, we helped him set up office here in our home so as many who wanted could receive adjustments from him. He saw about 40 different ones of the staff of Trans World Radio here in Bonaire. Then on his return visit, we helped him set up office in one of the buildings at TWR. That time he gave adjustments to about 50 of our staff.
>
> I could cite story after story of various ones he helped. It was just a beautiful time! We really thank the Lord for his ministry among us. We know he has helped to prevent illnesses in many instances. The insights he gave into living were also very mean-

ingful to many.

The patient that I am most excited about his helping is my husband, Joe, who had been bothered with a persistent stomach and intestinal problem off and on for 11 months. It was really becoming a hindrance to his effective work here. (He is an engineer working with the huge transmitters at the transmitter site.) Dr. Blossom really zeroed in on his problem, giving him several adjustments. Joe also had hip problems as well as difficulty in his upper neck. Since those adjustments in January, Joe has not been bothered at all. We truly thank the Lord for sending Dr. Blossom our way and for the effective way in which he ministered to us individually as well as to the staff.

We trust that it will work out for Dr. Blossom to visit Bonaire again and minister among us. He is truly a remarkable individual with a glowing Christian testimony. We thank the Lord for him. Sincerely, Mrs. Joseph H. Miller, Trans World Radio, Bonaire

From this very humble beginning, the short-term ministry of the Christian Chiropractors Association has grown tremendously until it is probably the largest ministry of the Association. Several hundred members have now gone into over a hundred different countries around the world. Many have gone several times and some plan to go someplace every year. There are two primary types of service which the short term missionary chiropractor has found to be very effective. The first is to serve the physical needs of the resident missionary. Most of these people have no chiropractor in their area and some have suffered for a long time waiting for one to come to visit them. Others have had to return to their homelands to seek help. When our short-term doctor arrives, he usually find himself very busy just taking care of other missionaries. Throughout this book, we have noted accounts of this service which short-term chiropractors have given to resident missionaries and the appreciation which the they have shown to the missionary chiropractor.

The other avenue of service, which has been very effective, is in church planting. We have found that the short-term missionary needs to align himself/herself with a resident missionary and have him/her announce ahead of time that:

An American Doctor of Chiropractic is coming to take care of headaches, backaches, arm and leg pains and many other health related problems. If you want to see the American Doctor, be at (such and such a place) on (which ever day or days that are planned).

When the doctor arrives, we schedule a national evangelist to be there to speak, preach, and/or hand out tracts all day long. We also need a secretary/counselor to take down names and make a record of everyone who comes. At the same time, inquiry should be made by this secretary, as to any decision or interest the patients may have in the message of the Gospel. Follow-up work should then be planned for the next several weeks after the doctors have moved on.

In this manner, we can plan on an average of 100 to 150 contacts per day, per doctor. It is not unusual for two doctors to minister to the needs of 3000 to 3500 people in a ten-day period, and if the follow-up work is successful, it is not impossible to start four or five new churches. The Director for the Word of Life Ministry in Poland, where this program has been followed very carefully, has said,

Give me two hundred chiropractors and I will evangelize the entire Nation of Poland.

In 1984, we made a trip to Montego Bay, Jamaica with a church group out of Pennsylvania. While on this trip we were able to serve in many schools and churches, both with chiropractic as well as preaching opportunities. It was on this trip that we met a tour guide named, Dudley Graham of Montego Bay. Dudley is a fine Christian gentleman and an elder in his church. He became very interested in what we had to offer and invited us to come back and bring more chiropractors with us next time. We did that later that year and over the last 18 years the C.C.A. has sent two or three teams of six to sixteen doctors, wives and support personal every year. Rev. and Mrs. Gordon Sandau, child evangelists now is their semi-retirement years, have traveled with our teams almost every year and have reported tremendous results, with literally thousands of spiritual decisions among the school children of Jamaica. Without the help, guidance and encouragement of Dudley Graham, this would not have been possible.

We have found that the Jamaica experience is an excellent *"boot camp."* The Jamaican people speak English so there is no language barrier and they are most appreciative of anything the Americans can do for them. We have always rented a private villa and this allows the team the security as well as the opportunity for training and fellowship for the team. At the same time the ministry with the people does offer a cross culture experience which most short-term beginners need.

In 1992, Rev. James Weber, our C.C.A. Missions Director, received an invitation to take a team to the Ukraine. The old Soviet Union was no more and a new sense of freedom had come to the people behind the old Iron Curtain. Jim organized a team of about 15 C.C.A. members and associates and they traveled the length of the country on a cruise ship on the Dnieper River, stopping in about ten cities along the way. In each city they had opportunity to visit churches, meet pastors and speak to Ukrainian Christians. From those contacts on that trip, it has opened many doors, as churches, pastors and Ukrainian Christians invited our members into their homes and churches. The C.C.A. has sponsored several teams each year with dozens of chiropractors as well as medical doctors, nurses and other health professionals going to that land which was so deprived of the Gospel for 75 years. The Christian Medical Society of Ukraine has been very much involved in our ministry and have welcomed us into hospitals and clinics as well as given us opportunities to speak at many of their conventions. Rev. Weber and his wife, Dorothy, have built strong friendships after their more than fifteen trips to Ukraine.

Several of our members have been there many times also and have developed a real bond with the Ukrainian people.

Short-Term Doctors

The following is a partial list of Doctors of Chiropractic who have served as short-term missionary chiropractors after the before mentioned early pioneers of this ministry. Not included in the list are the many spouses who also joined in the trips as well as the many other health professionals, pastors, and everyday christian workers who taught Bible lessons, preached, as well as painted, laid brick and dug ditches. Teams were organized with up to 35 in a team. The Jamaica teams usually involved eight people with at least 4 or 5 doctors. Rev. and Mrs. Gordon Sandau of Loveland, Colorado went to Jamaica at least 20 times and led the children's ministries. Only eternity will reveal the results of their dedicated work.

We have no way of knowing how many other members of the profession went with church teams or with other mission societies. The following is a list of current and past members that served either directly or indirectly on a Christian Chiropractors Association Short-Term trip..

1962-1990
Dr. Nyle Ziegler of Shippenville, PA made many trips to India, Haiti, Honduras, Ecuador, Brazil and Peru.

1969-1983
Dr. Rufus Lister of Atlanta, Georgia made 33 trips into Eastern Europe before the fall of the Soviet Union.

1981-1991
Dr. Gary Pierce Tucson, AZ Mexico (Each Month)
1968 & 1970
Dr. William Marshall Ottawa Lake, MI Abu Dabi, U.A.E.

1970
Dr. John Karr Tulsa, OK 70 s Several trips to Tribal Villages of South Africa
Dr. James Douglas Woodstock, Ontario New Guinea

1971
Dr. David Cox Monaco Yugoslavia, Bulgaria, Turkey, Iran & Afghanistan
1974
Dr. Al Anderson Huron, SD Africa

1975
Dr. Dan Schneider Nappanee, IN Guatemala

1976
Dr. Dan Schneider Nappanee, IN Guatemala

1978
Dr. Dan Schneider Nappanee, IN 7 Caribbean Countries
Dr. James Barton Arcadia, LA Mexico

1979
Dr. Dan Schneider Nappanee, IN West Indies
Dr. John Karr Tulsa, OK India & China

1980
Dr. C.W. Fambrough Ft. Charlotte, FL Chili
Dr. Dan Schneider Nappanee, IN Aruba

1981
Dr. John Karr Tulsa, OK South Africa
Dr. Harry Kalsbeek Castro Valley, CA Singapore, Taiwan, Philippines, Hong Kong
Dr. Jerald Balduf St. Petersburg, FL Bahamas

1982
Dr. Richard Craft Ellenville, NY Ghana
Dr. Robert Trigo Fullerton, CA Mexico

1983
Dr. Bruce Kniegge Anchorage, AK Ecuador
Dr. Dan Schneider Nappanee, IN Japan
Dr. Robert Trigo Fullerton, CA Honduras

1983, continued

Dr. Glenn Stillwagon	Monongahela, PA	Haiti
Dr. James Williams	Memphis, TN	Mexico
Dr. Lester Blank	Gap, PA	Mexico

1984

Dr. Glenn Hultgren	Fort Collins, CO	Jamaica & Haiti
Dr. Glenn Stillwagon	Monongahela, PA	Haiti
Dr. James Staub	Valparaiso, IN	Haiti
Dr. Wes Trout	Northumberland, PA	Haiti
Dr. Donald Waschler	S. Williamsport, PA	Haiti
Dr. Ralph Zewicki	Garden City, MI	Haiti
Dr. Dennis Baron	Howell, MI	Haiti
Dr. P. L. Silcox	Redford, MI	Haiti
Dr. Charles JangDhari	Bird-in-Hand, PA	Guatemala
Dr. Robert Trigo	Fullerton, CA	Mexico
Dr. Bruce Kniegge	Anchorage, AK	Ecuador
Dr. Margaret Strickland	Anchorage, AK	Ecuador

1985

Dr. Joseph Manthei	Drumore, PA	India
Dr. Mark Brett	Lake Orion, MI	Jamaica
Dr. David Wilson	Tillsonburg, Ontario	Jamaica
Dr. Fred Vlietstra	Middleton, NY	Jamaica
Dr. Naomi Brubaker	Lewistown, PA	Jamaica
Dr. Charles JangDhari	Bird-in-Hand, PA	Jamaica
Dr. Orville Churchill	Rogue River, OR	Jamaica
Dr. Dan Hagen	Sioux Center, SD	Jamaica
Dr. Robert Lech	Maplewood, NJ	Jamaica
Dr. Dan Schneider	Nappanee, IN	Chili & Argentina
Dr. David Carey	Placerville, CA	Mexico

1986

Dr. Robert Braile	Rockledge, FL	U.S.S.R.
Dr. Solomon Aordkian	Naugatuck, CT	Dominican Republic
Dr. Chester Smith	Parsippany, NJ	Jamaica
Dr. Glenn Hultgren	Fort Collins, CO	Jamaica
Dr. Charles JangDhari	Bird-in-Hand, PA	Jamaica
Dr. Naomi Brubaker	Lewistown, PA	Jamaica
Dr. Robert Lech	Maplewood, NJ	Jamaica
Dr. David Wade	Anniston, AL	Jamaica
Dr. Ernest Anrig	Fresno, CA	Jamaica
Dr. Orville Churchill	Rogue River, OR	Jamaica
Dr. Curtis Saunders	Devils Lake, ND	Jamaica
Dr. Mary Miller	W. Lafayette, IN	Jamaica
Dr. Bruce Hagen	Sioux Falls, SD	Jamaica
Dr. Daniel Hagen	Sioux Falls, SD	Jamaica
Rev. Gordon & Lois Sandau	Loveland, CO	Jamaica

1987

Dr. Solomon Aordkian	Naugatuck, CT	Antigua, W.I.
Dr. Ramon Barrero	Manteca, CA	Columbia
Dr. Dennis Greenlee	Lower Lake, CA	Ecuador
Dr. Glenn Nicholas	Reno, NV	Antigua, W.I.
Dr. Mark Brett	Lake Orion, MI	Jamaica
Dr. Curtis Saunders	Devils Lake, ND	Jamaica
Dr. William DeRegibus	Farmville, VA	Jamaica
Dr. Robert Starpoli	Blauvelt, NY	Jamaica
Dr. Dennis Severson	Augusta, WI	Jamaica
Dr. Glenn Sisk	Gilroy, CA	Jamaica
Dr. Bruce Hagen	Sioux Falls, SD	Jamaica
Dr. Glenn Hultgren	Fort Collins, CO	Jamaica
Dr. Lois Southern	Houston, TX	Jamaica
Phil Southern	Houston, TX	Jamaica
Dr. Jack Foughty	North Canton, OH	Jamaica
Dr. Ed Matheson	Traverse City, MI	Jamaica
Dr. Greg White	Fort Collins, CO	Jamaica
Dr. Chester Smith	Parsippany, NJ	Jamaica
Rev. Gordon & Lois Sandau	Loveland, CO	Jamaica
Dr. Donald Ping	Warren, IN	Philippines
Dr. Kenneth Luther	W. Los Angeles, CA	Mexico
Dr. Richard Schmelzle	Willowdale, Ontario	Korea, Philippines, Hong Kong
Dr. Robert Trigo	Santa Ana, CA	Honduras & Nicaragua

1988

Dr. Steven Huneycutt	Round Rock, TX	El Salvador
Dr. Rufus Lister	Atlanta, GA	Hungary
Dr. Fred Vlietstra	Middleton, NY	Grenada
Dr. Jerome Harold	Miami Shores, FL	Granada
Dr. Jim Patton	Yakima, WA	Israel
Dr. Dennis Greenlee	Lower Lake, CA	Ecuador
Dr. Charles Jang Dhari	Bird-in-Hand, PA	Poland
Dr. Scott Crill	Cupertino, CA	Columbia
Dr. William DeRegibus	Farmville, VA	Mexico
Dr. Mark Brett	Lake Orion, MI	Jamaica
Dr. Stuart Sultze	Bakersfield, CA	Jamaica
Dr. Bruce Hagen	Sioux Falls, SD	Jamaica
Beth Hagen	Sioux Falls, SD	Jamaica
Dr. Dan Schneider	Nappanee, IN	Jamaica
Dr. Glenn Sisk	Bellville, MI	Jamaica
Dr. Fred Vlietstra	Middleton, NY	Jamaica
Dr. Bruce Kniegge	Anchorage, AK	Jamaica
Dr. Alan Zelm	Stoughton, WI	Jamaica
JoAnn Zelm	Stoughton, WI	Jamaica
Dr. Karl Anderson	Kimball, MN	Jamaica
Rev. Gordon & Lois Sandau	Loveland, CO	Jamaica

1989

Dr. Deborah Halling	Medfield, MA	Haiti
Dr. David Ryan	Seattle, WA	Poland
Dr. Luis Ruis	Phoenix, AZ	Peru
Dr. Jim Patton	Southaven, MS	Mexico
Dr. R.E. Trigo	Huntington Bch, CA	Lebanon & Israel
Dr. Bruce Kniegge	Fort Collins, CO	Mexico
Dr. Steve Huneycutt	Round Rock, TX	Ecuador
Dr. Steven Sauder	Washington, IL	Ecuador
Dr. Richard Behrend	Jasper, MO	Mali, West Africa
Dr. Kevin Keough	Macon, MO	Ecuador
Dr. Ivan Ortman	Canistota, SD	Ecuador
Dr. Dennis Greenlee	Lower Lake, CA	Ecuador
Dr. Lyle Grenz	Lisbon, Portugal	Hungary, Bulgaria Czechoslovakia, Romania,
Dr. Gordon Heuser	Lee s Summit, MO	Korea & Philippines
Dr. Gordon Lawson	Canada	Columbia
Dr. Susan Lawson	Canada	Columbia
Dr. Jerry Whitehead	Perryton, TX	Jamaica
Dr. Sally Herman	Mt. Vernon, WA	Jamaica
Dr. Fred Vlietstra	Middleton, NY	Jamaica
Dr. Randy Miers	Farmville, VA	Jamaica
Dr. Brian Darrow	Frankfort, IN	Jamaica
Dr. Dale Hultgren	Dassel, MN	Jamaica
Dr. Janet Martin	Palm Harbor, FL	Jamaica
Dr. Patricia Allen	Coursegold, CA	Jamaica
Dr. Lois Southern	Houston, TX	Jamaica
Phil Southern	Houston, TX	Jamaica
Dr. Susan Rianda	Castro Valley, CA	Jamaica
Dr. Mark Brett	Lake Orion, MI	Jamaica
Dr. Bruce Kniegge	Fort Collins, CO	Jamaica
Rev. Gordon & Lois Sandau	Loveland, CO	Jamaica
Dr. William DeRegibus	Farmville, VA	Mexico
Dr. Dan Schneider	Elkhart, IN	Nevis

1990

Dr. Deborah Halling	Medfield, MA	Haiti
Dr. James Jorgenson	Peoria, AZ	Philippines
Dr. Tom Young	Lakeland, FL	Grenada
Dr. Ivan Christiansen	Wenatchee, WA	Chili
Dr. Ed. DeRegibus	Farmville, VA	Mexico
Dr. Jerome Harold	Miami Shores, FL	Romania
Dr. Reid Zentner	Hickory, NC	Kenya
Dr. James Eckert	Plymouth, MI	Guatemala
Dr. William DeRegibus	Farmville, VA	Guatemala
Dr. David Ryan	Seattle, WA	Poland
Dr. Ed Stephenson	Bryan, TX	Brazil
Dr. Stephen Anderson	Winslow, ME	Honduras

1990, continued

Dr. James Abler	Coon Rapids, MN	Ecuador
Dr. Glenn Sisk	Gilroy, CA	Mali & Niger, West Africa
Dr. Dan Schneider	Elkhart, IN	Romania & Hungary
Dr. Bruce Kniegge	Fort Collins, CO	Belize
Dr. Solomon Aordkian	Naugatuck, CT	Jamaica
Dr. John Krebs	Lexington, KY	Columbia
Dr. Ken Day	Stanwood, WA	Mexico
Dr. Susan Dejna	Greenfield, WI	Chili & Argentina
Dr. Lonnie Berger	Brandon, MN	Jamaica
Dr. Jeffrey Hartwell	Molalla, OR	Germany
Dr. Lois Southern	Houston, TX	Ecuador
Dr. Blanche Morse	Oregon	Brazil & Argentina
Dr. Charles Dunkerly	Sharon, PA	Dominican Republic
Dr. Karen Shields	Greenwich, CT	Ecuador
Dr. Ray Pope	Seattle, WA	Ecuador
Dr. Colin Wellum, Jr.	Burlington, Ontario	Haiti
Dr. Kevin Keough	Macon, MO	Ecuador
Dr. Fredrick Lewin	Owego, New York	Israel
Dr. Bruce Kniegge	Fort Collins, CO	Jamaica
Dr. Lois Southern	Houston, TX	Jamaica
Phil Southern	Houston, TX	Jamaica
Dr. Steve Taylor	Bothell, WA	Jamaica
Dr. Gordon Kaiser	DeWitt, AR	Jamaica
Dr. Bill Canaletti	Downey, CA	Jamaica
Dr. Michael DiMaio	Farmington, NY	Jamaica
Dr. Patricia Parker	Coarsegold, CA	Jamaica
Dr. Karen Shields	Greenwich, CT	Jamaica
Dr. Annette Stevko	Portland, OR	Jamaica
Dr. James Stilley	Norristown, PA	Jamaica
Dr. Lisa Casey	Flagstaff, AZ	Jamaica
Dr. Mark Brett	Lake Orion, MI	Jamaica
Dr. Stuart Kissinger	Simcoe, Ontario	Jamaica
Dr. Charles JangDhari	Bird-in-Hand, PA	Jamaica
Dr. Randolph Offner	Flagstaff, AZ	Jamaica
Dr. Mark Brett	Lake Orion, MI	Jamaica
Dr. Glenn Hultgren	Fort Collins, CO	Jamaica
Rev. Gordon & Lois Sandau	Loveland, CO	Jamaica
Dr. Leonard Heinrichs	Fresno, CA	Ukraine

1991

Dr. Stuart Sultze	Bakersfield, CA	Haiti
Dr. Ivan Ortman	Canistota, SD	Ecuador
Dr. David Madeira	Dallas, PA	St. Croix, W.I.
Dr. Brian Kalsbeek	Castro Valley, CA	Ecuador
Dr. Robert Smith	Winter Haven, FL	Ecuador & Nicaragua
Dr. Leonard Heinrichs	Fresno, CA	Belize
Dr. Brian Jensen	Belgrade, MT	Panama & Nicaragua

1991, continued

Dr. Kent Albrecht	Hattiesburg, MS	Honduras, Costa Rica
Dr. Lois Southern	Houston, TX	Ecuador
Dr. Ben Markham	Chattanooga, TN	Brazil
Dr. John Hall	Ottawa, Ontario	Columbia
Dr. Eric Jackson	Ottawa, Ontario	Columbia
Dr. Timothy Swihart	Ontario, CA	Russia, Poland, Hungary, Ukraine
Dr. Ted Stephenson	Bryan, TX	Russia, Poland, Hungary, Ukraine
Dr. Robert Smith	Winter Haven, FL	Jamaica
Barbara Smith	Winter Haven, FL	Jamaica
Dr. Deborah Halling	Medfield, MA	Haiti
Dr. Ted Stephenson	Bryan, TX	Brazil
Dr. John Gosche	Hailey, ID	Mexico (Every other month)
Dr. Ellictt Hays	Van Buren, AR	Guatemala
Dr. David Eisenberg	Lancaster, PA	Mexico
Dr. William DeRegibus	Farmville, VA	Guatemala
Dr. Nancy Carpentier	Portland, OR	Honduras & Nicaragua
Dr. Ranon Borrero	Bakersfield, CA	Mexico & Nicaragua
Dr. Andre KnustGraichen	San Jose, CA	Mexico
Dr. Stephen Anderson	Winslow, ME	Honduras
Dr. Bevis Bradtke	Australia	New Guinea
Dr. Carl Heigl	Racine, WI	Jamaica
Dr. Ted Gray	Standard, CA	Mexico
Dr. Gary Pierce	Oro Valley, AZ	Mexico
Dr. Glenn Hultgren	Fort Collins, CO	Jamaica
Dr. Scott Martin	Bryson City, NC	Jamaica
Dr. Patricia Parker	Coarsegold, CA	Jamaica
Dr. Charles Roost	Lansing, MI	Jamaica
Dr. Lois Southern	Houston, TX	Jamaica
Phil Southern	Houston, TX	Jamaica
Dr. Bruce Hagen	Sioux Falls, SD	Jamaica
Dr. Debe Williams	Jackson, TN	Jamaica
Dr. Alan Zelm	Stoughton, WI	Jamaica
Dr. Thomas Erndt	Sundburg, OH	Jamaica
Dr. Mark Brett	Lake Orion, MI	Jamaica
Rev. Gordon & Lois Sandau	Loveland, CO	Jamaica

1992

Dr. Stephen Anderson	Winslow, ME	India
Dr. John Williams	Canada	Jamaica
Dr. Stuart Kinsinger	Simcoe, Ontario	Jamaica
Dr. Ed Stephenson	Bryan, TX	Hungary, Ukraine Romania
Dr. Tim Swihart	Fort Wayne, IN	Romania
Dr. Dennis Greenlee	Lower Lake, CA	Ecuador
Dr. Orville Churchill	Rogue River, OR	Ecuador
Dr. Jerome Harold	Miami Shores, FL	Albania

1992, continued

Dr. Kelly Reed	Bakersfield, CA	Crow Indian Reservation, MT
Dr. Marc Sommer	Lincoln Park, NJ	Crow Indian Reservation, MT
Dr. William Kneebone	Martinez, CA	Brazil
Dr. Cathy Kneebone	Martinez, CA	Brazil
Dr. David Eisenberg	Lancaster, PA	Ecuador
Dr. Harry Kalsbeek	Castro Valley, CA	Switzerland
Dr. William Hollensed	Glen Ellyn, IL	Ecuador
Dr. Karen Shields	Greenwich, CT	Guatemala
Dr. Deborah Halling	Medfield, MA	Haiti & French Guiana
Dr. Richard Black	High Point, NC	Peru
Dr. Jim Williams	Tega City, SC	Hungary
Dr. Leonard Heinrichs	Fresno, CA	Belize
Dr. Herb Babcock	Pensacola, FL	Belize
Dr. Fred Vlietstra	Middleton, NY	Jamaica
Dr. Tim Swihart	Ontario, CA	Jamaica
Dr. Richard Banker	Spotsylvania, VA	Jamaica
Dr. Ann Guyot	Sevierville, TN	Jamaica
Dr. Scott Isaacson	Branfort, CT	Ukraine
Dr. Eric Gebhart	Freeport, TX	Ukraine
Dr. Lee Walden	Evansville, IN	Ukraine
Rev. Jim & Dot Weber	Fort Collins, CO	Ukraine
Dr. Daniel Hillis	Fort Lee, NJ	Mexico
Dr. Barry Sunshine	Knoxville, TN	Venezuela
Dr. Paul Carroccio	(Extended stay)	Israel
Dr. Ramon Borrero	Bakersfield, CA	Nicaragua
Dr. Robert Smith	Winter Haven, FL	Nicaragua
Dr. Ken Luther	Los Angeles, CA	Mexico

(Six Christian Students from Los Angeles Chiropractic College went with Dr. Luther)

Dr. Stuart Kinsinger	Simcoe, Ontario	Jamaica
Dr. Thomas Erndt	Sundbury, OH	Jamaica
Dr. Scott Martin	Bryon City, NC	Jamaica
Dr. Glenn Hultgren	Fort Collins, CO	Jamaica
Dr. Brian Scharf	Springville, NY	Jamaica
Dr. Alan Zelm	Stoughton, WI	Jamaica
Dr. Lois Southern	Houston, TX	Jamaica
Phil Southern	Houston, TX	Jamaica
Dr. James Fleming	Mountain Lake, MN	Jamaica
Dr. Carl Heigl	Racine, WI	Jamaica
Rev. Gordon & Lois Sandau	Loveland, CO	Jamaica

1993

Dr. Carl Heigl	Racine, WI	Ecuador
Dr. Ivan Ortman	Canistota, SD	Ecuador
Dr. Dennis Greenlee	Kelsey, CA	Ecuador
Dr. William T. Hendrick	Hartford, CT	Poland

1993, continued

Dr. Scott Martin	Bryson City, NC	Poland
Dr. George Curry	Windsor, CT	Poland
Dr, Andre KnustGraichen	San Jose, CA	Honduras
Dr. William DeRigibus	Farmville, VA	Guatemala
Dr. Glenn Hultgren	Fort Collins, CO	Ukraine
Rev. Jim & Dot Weber	Fort Collins, CO	Ukraine
Dr. Alan Zelm	Stoughton, WI	Ukraine
JoAnn Zelm	Stoughton, WI	Ukraine
Dr. Patrick McClure	Vista, CA	Ukraine
Dr. Bruce Hagen	Sioux Falls, SD	Ukraine
Beth Hagen	Sioux Falls, SD	Ukraine
Dr. Herb Schneider	Elkhart, IN	Ukraine
Dr. Dan Schneider	Elkhart, IN	Ukraine
Dr. Harry Kalsbeek	Castro Valley, CA	Ukraine
Dr. Doug Heise	Winter Park, FL	Ukraine
Dr. Lois Southern	Houston, TX	Ukraine
Phil Southern	Houston, TX	Ukraine
Dr. Adrian Doll	Los Angeles, CA	Ukraine
Dr. Keith McKim	Nampa, ID	Ukraine
Dr. Andre KnustGraichen	San Jose, CA	Ukraine
Dr. Brian Jensen	Whitehall, MT	Hungary
Dr. Doug Ripley	Watchung, NJ	Cuba
Dr. Richard Banker	Spotsylvania, VA	Cuba
Dr. Greg White	Fort Collins, CO	Nicaragua
Dr. Ed Stephenson	Bryon, TX	Brazil
Dr. Robert Smith	Winter Haven, FL	St. Kitts, W.I.
Dr. Ann Horstman	Sevierville, TN	Jamaica
Dr. Fred Vlietstra	Middleton, NY	Jamaica
Dr. Karen Mathiak	Griffin, GA	Jamaica
Dr. Kent Moore	Rogers, AR	Jamaica
Dr. Ed Carr	Fort Collins, CO	Jamaica
Dr. Richard Banker	Spotsylvania, VA	Jamaica
Rev. James Weber	Fort Collins, CO	Jamaica
Dr. Doug Ripley	Watchung, NJ	Jamaica
Dr. Bruce Hagen	Sioux Falls, SD	Jamaica
Dr. Thomas Fraus	Austin, TX	Jamaica
Dr. Glenn Hultgren	Fort Collins, CO	Jamaica
Rev. Gordon & Lois Sandau	Loveland, CO	Jamaica
Dr. Brian Scharf	Springville, NY	Jamaica
Dr. Lois Southern	Houston, TX	Jamaica
Phil Southern	Houston, TX	Jamaica
Dr. Leslie Quiram	Bloomington, IL	Jamaica
Dr. Randy Strange	Orange City, IA	Jamaica
Dr. Phillippe Selsis	Gladstone, Queensland	Poland
Dr. Gordon Heuser	Lee s Summit, MO	Philippines
Dr. Jerome Harold	Miami Shores, FL	Albania
Dr. Stuart Sultze	Bakersfield, CA	Guyana
Dr. Leonard Heinrichs	Clovis, CA	Hungary

1993, continued

Luella Heinrichs	Clovis, CA	Hungary
Dr. Van D. Merkle	Dayton, OH	Nepal
Dr. Mark Brett	Lake Orion, MI	Jamaica
Dr. Mark Zelm	Stoughton, WI	Jamaica
Dr. LeAnn Hildreth	Altamonte Springs, FL	Jamaica
Dr. Louis Vastola	Manchester, VT	Jamaica
Dr. John Octavi	Gahanna, OH	Jamaica

1994

Dr. Ivan Ortman	Canistota, SD	Ecuador
Dr. Stephen Anderson	Winslow, ME	Ecuador
Dr. Ed Matheson	Traverse City, MI	Grand Cayman
Dr. Joel Stuart	Redmond, OR	Madagascar
Dr. William Marshall	Fort Worth, TX	Germany & Ukraine
Dr. Richard Banker	Spotsylvania, VA	Cuba
Dr. Ann Horstman	Sevierville, TN	Jamaica
Dr. Karen Mathiak	Griffin, GA	Jamaica
Dr. David Graber	Marion, IA	Jamaica
Dr. Steve Salyers	Bakersfield, CA	Jamaica
Dr. Greg Heyart	Bakersfield, CA	Jamaica
Dr. Robert Smith	Winter Haven, FL	Jamaica
Dr. Robert Hoagland	Robinson, IL	Jamaica
Rev. Gordon & Lois Sandau	Loveland, CO	Jamaica
Dr. Bruce Hagen	Sioux Falls, SD	Jamaica
Dr. Lois Southern	Houston, TX	Jamaica
Phil Southern	Houston, TX	Jamaica
Dr. Darren Bell	Derby, NY	Jamaica
Dr. Linda Bruinsma	Wyoming, MI	Jamaica
Dr. Thomas Feldman	Wooster, OH	Jamaica
Dr. James Fleming	Mountain Lake, MN	Jamaica
Dr. Brian Scharf	Springville, NY	Jamaica
Dr. Gerald Zelm	Oconomowoc, WI	Jamaica
Dr. David Baker	Woodsfield, OH	Jamaica
Dr. William Marshall	Ottawa, MI	Ukraine
Dr. Deborah Halling	Haiti	Zaire
Dr. Marvin Speckman	Litchfield, MN	Ukraine
Dr. Harry Kalsbeek	Castro Valley, CA	Ukraine
Rev. James Weber	Fort Collins, CO	Ukraine
Dr. Glenn Hultgren	Fort Collins, CO	Ukraine
Dr. Bernard Kaseman	Moorhead, MN	Maldova & Russia
Dr. Ted Stephenson	Bryon, TX	Romania
Dr. Dr. Marc Sommer	Lincoln Park, NJ	Crow Indian Reservation, MT
Dr. Susan Dejna	Milwaukee, WI	Canadian Indians
Dr. Van D. Merkle	Dayton, OH	China
Dr. David Eisenberg	Lancaster, PA	Hungary
Dr. Leonard Heinrichs	Clovis, CA	Hungary
Dr. Dan Schneider	Elkhart, IN	Hungary

1994, continued

Dr. Anna Allan	El Paso, TX	Mexico
Dr. Howard Brown	Sidney, NE	Mexico
Dr. Andre KnustGraichen	San Jose, CA	Mexico

1995

Dr. Edwin Berry	Shrewsbury, MA	Jamaica
Dr. Philip Horner	West Perth, WA	Jamaica
Dr. Alan Bush	Waynesville, NC	Jamaica
Dr. Greg Cerrato	Tarpon Springs, FL	Jamaica
Dr. James Fleming	Mountain Lake, MN	Jamaica
Dr. Terra Fleming	Blaine, MN	Jamaica
Dr. David Graber	Marion, IA	Jamaica
Dr. Robert Hoaglund	Robinson, IL	Jamaica
Dr. Michael McCartney	Scottsdale, AZ	Jamaica
Dr. Carmel Raihala	Green Bay, WI	Jamaica
Dr. Fred Vlietstra	Middleton, NY	Jamaica
Dr. Brian Scharf	Springville, NY	Jamaica
Dr. Mark Zelm	Stoughton, WI	Jamaica
Rev. Gordon & Lois Sandau	Loveland, CO	Jamaica
Dr. Harry Kalsbeek	Castro Valley, CA	Ukraine
Dr. Dan Hanson	San Lorenzo, CA	Ukraine
Dr. Merry Harris	Lynnwood, WA	Ukraine
Dr. Leonard Heinrichs	Clovis, CA	Ukraine
Rev. James Weber	Fort Collins, CO	Ukraine
Dr. Doug Heise	Winter Park, FL	Ukraine
Dr. Chester Smith	Parsippany, NJ	Ukraine
Dr. James Fleming	Mountain Lake, MN	Ukraine
Dr. L. Mark Brett	Lake Orion, MI	Ukraine
Dr. Jodi Forcey	Clearfield, PA	Ukraine
Dr. Jack Manuele	Glendale, CA	Ukraine
Barbara Manuele	Glendale, CA	Ukraine
Christy Evans	Placentia, CA	Ukraine
Dr. Derek Taylor	Huron, OH	Ukraine
Dr. Lois Southern	Houston, TX	Ukraine
Phil Southern	Houston, TX	Ukraine
Dr. Alan Zelm	Stoughton, WI	Poland
JoAnn Zelm	Stoughton, WI	Poland
Dr. Bruce Hagen	Sioux Falls, SD	Poland
Beth Hagen	Sioux Falls, SD	Poland
Dr. Gerald Zelm	Oconomowoc, WI	Poland
Dr. Tom Feldman	Wooster, OH	Poland
Dr. Stanley Lindblom	Sidney, MT	Ecuador & Bolivia
Dr. Thomas Paulos	Marietta, GA	Nicaragua
Dr. Marc Sommer	Lincoln Park, NJ	Crow Indian Reservation, MT
Dr. James Tassel	Cincinnati, OH	Hungary
Dr. Derek Taylor	Huron, OH	Mexico
Dr. Nate Wirt	Seabrook, TX	Bolivia

1995, continued

Dr. Stanley Lindblom	Sidney, MT	Bolivia
Lillian Lindblom	Sidney, MT	Bolivia

1996

Dr. Richard Banker	Spotsylvania, VA	Cuba
Dr. Mark Brett	Lake Orion, MI	Israel
Dr. Dr. Linda Bruinsma	Wyoming, MI	Ukraine
Dr. Glenn Hultgren	Fort Collins, CO	Ukraine
Dr. Harry Kalsbeek	Castro Valley, CA	Ukraine
Dr. Jack Manuele	Glendale, CA	Ukraine
Barbara Manuele	Glendale, CA	Ukraine
Christy Evans	Placentia, CA	Ukraine
Dr. Sharon Epperson	Ceres, CA	Ukraine
Dr. Chuck Roost	Lansing, MI	Ukraine
Dr. Chester Smith	Parsippany, NJ	Ukraine
Rev. Jim & Dot Weber	Fort Collins, CO	Ukraine
Dr. William Marshall	Fort Worth, TX	Ukraine
Dr. Brian Scharf	Springville, NY	Jamaica
Dr. Orville Churchill	Baker City, OR	Jamaica
Dr. Jerry Spanton	England	Jamaica
Dr. Randal Stange	Orange City, IA	Jamaica
Dr. Emilie Leber	Beecher, IL	Jamaica
Dr. Timothy Swihart	Fort Wayne, IN	Jamaica
Dr. Carmel Raihala	Green Bay, WI	Jamaica
Dr. David Baker	Woodsfield, OH	Jamaica
Dr. Jack Foughty	N. Canton, OH	Jamaica
Dr. Robert Hoagland	Robinson, IL	Jamaica
Dr. Lois Southern	Houston, TX	Jamaica
Phil Southern	Houston, TX	Jamaica
Rev. Gordon & Lois Sandau	Loveland, CO	Jamaica
Dr. James Fleming	Mountain Lake, MN	Philippines
Dr. Randall Graham	Bakersfield, CA	Poland
Dr. Alan Zelm	Stoughton, WI	Poland
Dr. Bruce Hagen	Sioux Falls, SD	Poland
Dr. Scott Martin	Bryson City, NC	Poland
Dr. Jack Manuele	Glendale, CA	Ecuador
Barbara Manuele	Glendale, CA	Ecuador
Dr. John Needler	Columbus Grove, OH	Dominican Republic
Dr. Ivan Ortman	Canistota, SD	Ecuador
Dr. James Tassell	Bellefontaine, OH	Hungary
Dr. Derek Taylor	Huron, OH	Ecuador

1997

Dr. Stephen Anderson	Winslow, ME	Dominican Republic
Dr. Edward Boren	Easley, SC	Jamaica
Dr. L. Mark Brett	Lake Orion, MI	Jamaica
Dr. Alan Bush	Waynesville, NC	Jamaica
Dr. Brian Scharf	Springville, NY	Jamaica

1997, continued

Lynn Reusser	Woodsfield, OH	Jamaica
Dr. Robert Hoagland	Robinson, IL	Jamaica
Dr. James Mattern	West Lafayette, IN	Jamaica
Dr. Donald Selvidge	Mattoon, IL	Jamaica
Dr. Lois Southern	Houston, TX	Jamaica
Phil Southern	Houston, TX	Jamaica
Dr. Joe O Donnell	York, PA	Jamaica
Rev. Gordon & Lois Sandau	Loveland, CO	Jamaica
Dr. Sharon Epperson	Ceres, CA	Ukraine
Wayne Aupperle	Ceres, CA	Ukraine
Dr. Brenda Dukes	Plant City, FL	Ukraine
Dr. James Fleming	Mountain Lake, MN	Ukraine
Dr. Jack Manuele	Glendale, CA	Ukraine
Barbara Manuele	Glendale, CA	Ukraine
Christy Evans	Placentia, CA	Ukraine
Rev. Jim & Dot Weber	Fort Collins, CO	Ukraine
Dr. Nate Wirt	Seabrook, TX	Ukraine
Dr. Glenn Hultgren	Fort Collins, CO	Ukraine
Dr. L. Mark Brett	Lake Orion, MI	Ukraine
Dr. Cary Yurkiw	Canada	Ukraine
Dr. Dennis Yurkiw	Canada	Ukraine
Dr. David Eisenberg	Lancaster, PA	Hungary & Romania
Dr. Thomas Feldman	Wooster, OH	Poland
Dr. Marc Sommer	Lincoln Park, NJ	Crow Indian Reservation, MT
Dr. James Fleming	Mountain Lake, MN	Crow Indian Reservation, MT
Dr. W. Charles Hollensed	Glen Ellyn, IL	Ecuador
Dr. Cecil McLeod	Anchorage, AK	Honduras
Dr. Zsolt M ller	Hutchinson, MN	Hungary
Dr. Mona Ruse	Allegan, MI	Mexico
Dr. James Tassell	Bellefontaine, OH	Hungary
Dr. Louis Vastola	Manchester, VT	Hungary
Dr. Alan Zelm	Stoughton, WI	Poland
Dr. Bruce Hagen	Sioux Falls, SD	Poland
Dr. Randall Graham	Bakersfield, CA	Poland
Dr. Ed Carr	Fort Collins, CO	Guatemala
Dr. Jack Manuele	Glendale, CA	Ecuador
Barbara Manuele	Glendale, CA	Ecuador

1998

Dr. Carl Anderson		Poland
Dr. Michael Bagnell	Coral Gables, FL	Jamaica
Dr. Brian Scharf	Springville, NY	Jamaica
Dr. David Baker	Woodsfield, OH	Jamaica
Dr. Mike Cory	Marietta, GA	Jamaica
Lynn Reusser	Woodsfield, OH	Jamaica
Dr. Katharine Mann	Brooklyn, NY	Jamaica

1998, continued

Dr. Zsolt M ller	Hutchinson, MN	Jamaica
Renae M ller	Hutchinson, MN	Jamaica
Dr. Glenn Nicholas	Lewiston, ID	Jamaica
Laural Nicholas	Lewiston, ID	Jamaica
Dr. Bruce Kniegge	La Paz, Bolivia	Jamaica
Katie Kniegge	La Paz, Bolivia	Jamaica
Dr. Doug Ripley	Beachwood, NJ	Jamaica
Dr. Fred Vlietstra	Middleton, NY	Jamaica
Dr. Matthew Mora	Huntington Beach, CA	Jamaica
Dr. Dan Robinson	Waldorf, MD	Jamaica
Dr. Mitch DeValliere	Reno, NV	Jamaica
Rev. Gordon & Lois Sandau	Loveland, CO	Jamaica
Dr. L. Mark Brett	Lake Orion, MI	Ukraine
Dr. James Fleming	Mountain Lake, MN	Ukraine
Dr. Glenn Hultgren	Fort Collins, CO	Ukraine
Dr. Travis Park	Plano, TX	Ukraine
Dr. Chester Smith	Parsippany, NJ	Ukraine
Dr. James Spertzel	Biglerville, PA	Ukraine
Rev. Jim & Dot Weber	Fort Collins, CO	Ukraine
Dr. Charles JangDhari	Poland	Ukraine
Dr. James Fleming	Mountain Lake, MN	Philippines
Dr. Tom Feldman	Wooster, OH	Poland
Dr. Charles Feldman	Wooster, OH	Poland
Dr. Bruce Hagen	Sioux Falls, SD	Poland
Dr. Marc Sommer	Lincoln Park NJ	Crow Indian Reservation, MT
Dr. Jim Lowrance	Las Vegas, NV	Bulgaria
Dr. Bob Purcell		Bulgaria
Dr. Jack Manuele	Glendale, CA	Ecuador
Barbara Manuele	Glendale, CA	Ecuador
Dr. Ivan Ortman	Canistota, SD	Ecuador
Dr. Jeanette Pena	San Bernardino, CA	Columbia
Dr. Fred Vlietstra	Middleton, NY	Honduras
Dr. Phillip Yoo	Duluth, GA	Honduras
Dr. Chuck Roost	Lansing, MI	Brazil
Dr. Herb Schneider	Elkhart, IN	Barbados
Dr. George Harris	Agoura Hills, CA	Belize
Dr. James Waddel	Macon, GA	Romania
Dr. Richard Banker	Spotsylvania, VA	Cuba

1999

Dr. Ron Adams	Jackson, MI	New Guinea
Dr. Roger Bailey	Nashville, TN	Romania
Dr. Donna Ransdell	Huber Heights, OH	Nairobi
Dr. Grace Cobian	Lancaster, PA	Jamaica
Dr. Bruce Kniegge	Fort Collins, CO	Jamaica
Dr. Fred Vlietstra	Middleton, NY	Jamaica
Suzanne Vlietstra	Middleton, NY	Jamaica

1999, continued

Rev. Gordon & Lois Sandau	Loveland, CO	Jamaica
Dr. Donn Innaimo	Watertown, CT	Jamaica
Rev. Jim & Dot Weber	Fort Collins, CO	Ukraine
Dr. Christine Cook	Lake Oswego, OR	Ukraine
Joseph Cook	Lake Oswego, OR	Ukraine
Dr. Tom Feldman	Wooster, OH	Ukraine
Dr. Doug Heise	Winter Park, FL	Ukraine
Dr. DeWayne Mirtsching	Austin, TX	Ukraine
Dr. Travis Park	Plano, TX	Ukraine
Dr. Glenn Hultgren	Fort Collins, CO	Ukraine
Dr. Chester Smith	Parsippany, NJ	Ukraine
Dr. Jim Spertzel	Biglerville, PA	Ukraine
Dr. Charles JangDhari	Poland	Ukraine
Dr. Susan Dejna	Milwaukee, WI	Argentina & Chili
Dr. Patrick Delamere	Mahopac, NY	Siberia
Dr. Daniel Holt	Juneau, AK	Siberia
Dr. Greg Heyart	Bakersfield, CA	Nigeria
Dr. Steve Jennings	Rensselaer, IN	Kenya
Dr. David Eisenberg	Lancaster, PA	Poland
Dr. Tom Feldman	Wooster, OH	Poland
Dr. Rick Puchta	Kalispell, MT	Poland
Dr. Gerald Zelm	Oconomowoc, WI	Poland
Dr. Paul Smith	Madison, WI	Poland
Dr. Charles JangDhari	Krakow, Poland	Kosovo
Dr. Marc Sommer	Lincoln Park, NJ	Crow Indian Reservation, MT
Dr. Scott Goldsmith	Lancaster, PA	Crow Indian Reservation, MT
Dr. Randall Graham	Bakersfield, CA	Guyana
Dr. Debra Halling	Haiti	Poland
Dr, Greg Heyart	Bakersfield, CA	Belize
Dr. Travis Park	Plano, TX	Honduras
Dr. David Ridge	Keene, NH	India
Dr. Tim Streit	Penang, Malaysia	India
Dr. Steve Salyers	Bakersfield, CA	Belize
Dr. Dan Schneider	Elkhart, IN	Panama
Dr. Tim Tassell	Bellefontaine, OH	Hungary
Dr. William Hendrick	East Hampton, CT	Hungary

2000

Dr. Woodrow Beck	Lumberton, NC	Jamaica
Dr. Steven Guagliardo	Staten Island, NY	Jamaica
Dr. Katharine Mann	Brooklyn, NY	Jamaica
Dr. Dennis Reiff	Lansdale, PA	Jamaica
Dr. Brian Scharf	Springville, NY	Jamaica
Dr. Matthew Skaff	Omaha, NE	Jamaica
Deanna Skaff	Omaha, NE	Jamaica
Dr. Fred Vlietstra	Middleton, NY	Jamaica

2000, continued

Suzanne Vlietstra	Middleton, NY	Jamaica
Lynn Reusser	Woodsfield, OH	Jamaica
Dr. Kurt Brzezinski	Emmaus, PA	Venezuela
Dr. Randall Graham	Bakersfield, CA	Venezuela
Dr. Grace Cobian	Lancaster, PA	Ukraine
Dr. Doug Heise	Winter Haven, FL	Ukraine
Dr. Tom Feldman	Hudson, OH	Ukraine
Dr. James Fleming	Mountain Lake, MN	Ukraine
Dr. Robert Jensen	Stewartville, MN	Ukraine
Dr. Julie Niedwick	Mechanicsburg, PA	Ukraine
Mark Niedwick	Mechanicsburg, PA	Ukraine
Dr, Travis Park	Escondido, CA	Ukraine
Dr. David Parker	Ephrata, PA	Ukraine
Dr. James Spertzel	Biglerville, PA	Ukraine
Rev. Jim & Dot Weber	Fort Collins, CO	Ukraine
Dr. Dale Williams	Roxboro, NC	Ukraine
Dr. Jennifer Murphy	Pink Hill, NC	Ukraine
Lynn Reusser	Woodsfield, OH	Ukraine
Dr. Charles JangDhari	Krakow, Poland	Ukraine
Dr. Bill Decken	Spartanburg, SC	Belize
Dr. Tom Feldman	Hudson, OH	Poland
Dr. Greg Heyart	Bakersfield, CA	Nicaragua
Dr. Steve Salyers	Bakersfield, CA	Nicaragua
Dr. Willard Smith	Rock Island, IL	Bolivia
Dr. Marc Sommer	Lincoln Park, NJ	Crow Indian Reservation, MT
Dr. DeWayne Mirtsching	Austin, TX	Crow Indian Reservation, MT
Dr. Kelly Reed	Bakersfield, CA	Crow Indian Reservation, MT
Dr. Gary Rock	Puyallup, WA	Crow Indian Reservation, MT
Dr. Greg Heyart	Bakersfield, CA	Nigeria
Dr. David Richardson	Tuscaloosa, AL	Mexico
Dr. Nicole Nygren	Van Wert, OH	Mexico
Dr. Derek Taylor	Torrance, CA	Mexico
Dr. Charles Roost	Lansing, MI	Hungary
Dr. Charles JangDhari	Krakow, Poland	Kosovo
Dr. Tim Striet	Penang, Malaysia	Indonesia

2001

Dr. Fred Vlietstra Suzanne Vlietstra	Middleton, NY	Togo & Benin, West Africa
Dr. Willard Smith	Rock Island, IL	Ethiopia
Dr. Greg White	Fort Collins, CO	Ethiopia
Dr. Glenn Hultgren	Fort Collins, CO	Ethiopia
Dr. Wayne Stump	Phoenix, AZ	Mexico
Dr. Greg Heyart	Bakersfield, CA	Peru

2001, continued

Dr. Marc Sommer	Lincoln Park, NJ	Crow Indian Reservation, MT
Dr. Gary Rock	Puyallup, WA	Crow Indian Reservation, MT
Dr. Willard Smith	Rock Island, IL	Haiti
Dr. Thomas Pamer	Mansfield, OH	Poland
Dr. Tom Feldman	Hudson, OH	Poland
Dr. Richard Callahan	York, NE	Poland
Dr. James Fleming	Mountain Lake, MN	Ukraine
Dr. Doug Heise	Winter Haven, FL	Ukraine
Dr. Ed Fleming	Indialantic, FL	Ukraine
Dr. Brian Scharf	Springville, NY	Ukraine
Dr. James Spertzel	Biglerville, PA	Ukraine
Dr. Grace Cobian	Lancaster, PA	Ukraine
Dr. Sharon Epperson	Ceres, CA	Ukraine
Wayne Aupperle	Ceres, CA	Ukraine
Dr. Aron Enns	Abbotsford, BC, Canada	Ukraine
Vonnie Enns	Abbotsford, BC, Canada	Ukraine
Rev. Jim & Dot Weber	Fort Collins, CO	Ukraine
Dr. Charles JangDhari	Krakow, Poland	Ukraine
Dr. David Eisenberg	Lancaster, PA	Bosnia
Dr. Charles JangDhari	Krakow, Poland	Kosovo
Dr. Steve Jennings	Rensselaer, IN	Kenya
Dr. Ken Plaut	Ojai, CA	Kazakastan
Dr. Brian Scharf	Springville, NY	Jamaica
Dr. Craig Honer	San Antonio, TX	Jamaica
Dr. Katharine Mann	Centerpoint, NY	Jamaica
Dr. Steven Kloster	Smith Center, KS	Jamaica
Dr. Fred Vlietstra	Middletown, NY	Jamaica
Suzanne Vlietstra	Middleton, NY	Jamaica
Dr. Willard Smith	Rock Island, IL	Jamaica
Dr. Charles Jackson	Grand Blanc, MI	Jamaica
Dr. Cecil McLeod	Anchorage, AK	Jamaica
Dr. Jackie McKool	Charleston, SC	Jamaica
Dr. Nancy Porter	Chico, CA	Jamaica

2002

Dr. Richard Puchta	Kalispell, MT	Bolivia
Dr. Willard Smith	Rock Island, IL	Bolivia
Dr. Grace Cobian	Lancaster, PA	Ukraine
Dr. James Spertzel	Biglerville, PA	Ukraine
Dr. Michael McCartney	Scottsdale, AZ	Mexico
Dr. Greg Heyart	Bakersfield, CA	Nigeria
Dr. Sharon Epperson	Cere, CA	Ukraine
Wayne Aupperle	Ceres, CA	Ukraine
Dr. Harvey Feenstra	Cortland, OH	Brazil
Dr. Tom Feldman	Stoughton, WI	Poland
Rev. Jim & Dot Weber	Fort Collins, CO	Ukraine

2002, continued

Dr. David Ridge	Keene, NH	China
Dr. Jack Manuele	Glendale, CA	Ecuador
Barbara Manuele	Glendale, CA	Ecuador
Dr. Doug Heise	Winter Haven, FL	Ukraine
Dr. Alphaes Thornton	Independence, OR	Ukraine
Dr. Stephen Smith	Jacksonville, FL	Ukraine
Dr. Doug Williams	Ontario, OR	Ukraine
Donna Williams	Ontario, OR	Ukraine
Dr. Tom Feldman	Stoughton, WI	Ukraine
Dr. Marc Sommer	Oakland, NJ	Crow Indians
Dr. Wayne Stump	Phoeniz, AZ	Mexico
Dr. Zsolt M ller	Eden Prairie, MN	Brazil
Dr. Gerald Zelm	Oconomowoc, WI	Poland
Dr. Tom Potisk	S. Milwaukie, WI	Poland
Dr. Fred Vlietstra	Middletown, NY	Jamaica
Suzanne Vlietstra	Middletown, NY	Jamaica
Dr. Chuck Vallee	Sherrill, NY	Jamaica
Dr. Doug Ripley	Toms River, NJ	Jamaica
Dr. Willard Smith	Rock Island, IL	Jamaica
Dr. Brian Scharf	Springville, NY	Jamaica
Dr. Craig Honer	San Antonio, TX	Jamaica
Dr. Katharine Mann	Centerpoint, NY	Jamaica
Dr. Matthew Gallager	Bloominton, MN	Jamaica

2003

Dr. William Hollensed	Glen Ellyn, IL	Peru
Lorna Hollensed	Glen Ellyn, IL	Peru
Dr. Grace Cobian	Lancaster, PA	Ukraine
Dr. James Spertzel	Biglerville, PA	Ukraine
Dr. Susanne Coffee	Charlottesville, VA	Honduras
Dr. Lee Popwell	Jacksonville, FL	Uganda
Dr. Gerald Zelm	Oconomowoc, WI	Poland
Dr. Greg Heyart	Bakersville,CA	Nigeria
Dr. Marc Sommer	Lincoln Park, NJ	Crow Indian Reservation, MT

It is not our intention to omit the name of any of our members who have made short-term mission trips, but that may be inevitable. The number of people involved in this program is so large that it is very possible that we have neglected to mention someone. This was not intentional and we are sorry if that happened. At the same time we know that many of the above made more than one trip in a year to the same land. This was not mentioned either, although the Lord surely knows and He will reward them accordingly. Likewise, we know that many a faithful spouse also went along and aided in various ways and many others stayed home and prayed for the success of their doctor spouse. These also should have special mention.

Not to be forgotten is the tremendous work involved in the C.C.A. Home Office by the faithful and dedicated staff who made all of the arrangements, bought the airplane tickets, hotel reservations, insurance and in general tried to make each trip a special success, both for the doctors involved but also for the missionaries and nationals whom they served.

The Short-Term Mission Program of the Christian Chiropractors Association is open to members of the C.C.A. only, and only after they have been in private practice for a period of two years or more. However, many supportive personal have been invited to join in some of these short-term mission assignments by affiliating with the C.C.A. as associate members. These have included nurses, medical doctors, ophthalmologists, orthopedic surgeons, audiologists, mid-wives, as well as various tradesmen, pastors and Bible teachers. They must pay their own way through donations to the C.C.A. The organization then makes all arrangements, buys the airline tickets, and the insurance necessary for personal protection. Then upon return, the short-term missionary must make a complete report of his/her daily activities during his trip.

In recent years, there have been more Doctors of Chiropractic setting up practice in third world countries than there were in the early years of the C.C.A. With the doctors establishing a commercial practice, there soon are laws protecting the practice of chiropractic in that country. This presents several problems for the short-term missionary chiropractor. We do not want to violate any laws in these countries and as it usually is not possible for our short-term doctors to get licensed in the country, they are limited in what they can do. The patients that our doctors treat are usually indigents who have no ability to pay, and therefore, do not pose a threat to the practice of the established doctor. However, if our doctors would be taking care of patients who could go to a resident doctor and could afford to pay for the service, we do not want our short-term doctors to serve in that capacity and thus create an estranged relationship with the resident doctor.

If the country has a licensing law, it may be necessary to get a short-term non-resident license by reciprocity. Many times we have found that the resident chiropractor is happy for the short-term doctor coming, because he knows he will get many referrals from contacts which the short-term doctors have made. Also she/he knows that he can get an adjustment for himself while they are there. In any case, the policy of the Christian Chiropractors Association is to be as careful as possible to not infringe on the rights of a resident doctor and yet to offer service to those who cannot in any other way get this service.

In the early years of the Association, it was impossible to find a mission which would allow a Doctor of Chiropractic to serve with their mission and use his professional training as part of that mission activity. The professional jealousy (on the part of the established medical personal) was so strong in those years that some of our members were prevented from practicing chiropractic and some were expelled from the mission for practicing chiropractic. Now, fifty years later, it is impossible to find enough Doctors of Chiropractic to go to fill all of the requests which come from individual missionaries and from mission societies for both short-term and resident missionary status.

We can only say again, "Against All Odds ... BUT GOD!"

Staff

Over the years several people other than the member doctors, have helped to make the Christian Chiropractors Association move, go, grow, and serve as God intended it to do. It is not possible to recognize all of them, but it is right that some should be mentioned.

Janet Lee Bray

The first paid staff of the Christian Chiropractors Association was Miss Janet Lee Bray. In 1961 Janet began working part-time as my office secretary/receptionist and part-time as C.C.A. secretary. As time went on, the C.C.A. work continued to grow, as did my practice. Janet's C.C.A. duties grew, and I hired other women to work in my practice.

Janet was a most faithful, dedicated employee. Everyone in the association loved her, and she built personal relationships with many of our members that have lasted over the years. Janet always added a personal touch to the C.C.A. correspondence and monthly newsletter.

As the C.C.A. office moved out of my clinic and into larger quarters, Janet moved

Blanche & Janet Bray

with it, and her work was designated as full-time C.C.A. In 1975 the C.C.A. office moved into the garden level basement of the home that Janet shared with her mother. At that time her mother, Blanche, also joined the staff, first as a volunteer and later as part-time employee. She helped run the printing press and did other office duties.

Janet's health was never good due to hyperthyroidism in her teen-age years. Surgery for the problem was not successful, and as years went by, her health became more of a problem. By 1989, she could no longer keep up with the stress and strain of the work; she had to retire and go on disability. Her heart still is with the ministry of the Christian Chiropractors Association. She gave 28 years to this ministry and all of the members of the C.C.A. thank God for her sacrificial, dedicated service.

Cecil L. Manewal

In March 1976 Mr. Cecil Manewal became C.C.A.'s first Executive Director. "Cec" had just retired, and although he was over 65, he did not intend to sit around doing nothing.

He had a rich background in business as a realtor, car dealer, savings and loan officer, and nursing home administrator. He was an active leader in a large church as an adult Sunday school teacher and the church moderator.

Cec was a real go-getter, wound up tight, and ready to fire at a moment's notice. He brought real spark to the association and soon endeared himself to many of our members. He was an avid golfer and a motorcycle buff.

Cec traveled around the country

Cecil "Cec" Manewal

visiting our members, attending association meetings, and promoting the C.C.A. at every opportunity. His devotional articles in the newsletter were inspirational as well as thought provoking for everyone. Cec did much to develop our annual conventions and secure speakers. He served as moderator for all of our meetings, and his humor and outgoing personality will be remembered by all.

Cec's health began to fail, and it was necessary for him to retire in 1985. He died of cancer in January 1987. Those of us who knew him, will not soon forget our great friend and fellow servant of the Lord, Cec Manewal.

Rev. Ronald Murphy

When Cec retired, Rev. Ronald Murphy assumed the position of Executive Director. Ron had pastored several churches and brought with him the experience of pastor and counselor. Ron's strengths lie in theological discussion and spiritual leadership. He brought a certain stable Biblical basis to our organization. Ron could speak to pastors as well as leaders of mission societies on their level.

Rev. Ronald Murphy

After seven years with the C.C.A, Rev. Ron realized that his real calling was church ministry, and he returned to the pastorate of a local congregation.

Rev. James Weber

Rev. James Weber joined the C.C.A. staff in February 1991 as part-time Director of Missions. Jim and his wife, Dorothy, had spent over 20 years in Japan with the Conserva-

tive Baptist Foreign Mission Board. Upon returning from Japan, they traveled the country helping churches develop and expand their missions outreach through a program the Webers developed called "Ministering in Missions." Rev. Jim also wrote a book, *Let's Quit Kidding Ourselves About Missions.*

Rev. Weber has opened many doors for the C.C.A. missions program. He has been especially involved in helping the evangelical church emerge in Ukraine and Eastern Europe and has led close to twenty short-term C.C.A. mission groups into Eastern

Rev. James Weber

Europe since he joined the C.C.A. staff. He has coordinated short-term ministries into many countries around the world and has secured medical doctors, dentists, nurses, midwives, orthopedic surgeons, audiologists, pastors, housewives and skilled laborers to make up short-term teams to go along with our doctors of chiropractic. He has seen first hand how Christian doctors can bring people into the church and how the pastors and church members in Eastern Europe welcome and are blessed by the doctors' presence.

During the 1990s, one of Jim's biggest projects was gathering and sending medical supplies, food, and clothing to Ukraine. Jim secured donations of medical and dental supplies and equipment, as well as food and clothing. He packed seven containers for shipment to Ukraine where Christian friends he had met over there distributed everything to those in need.

Jim has turned the situation that he found–that of no mission association wanting doctors of chiropractic–to a situation of having far more requests for doctors than we can fill.

Robert M. Hultgren

In 1989 Bob Hultgren joined the C.C.A. as comptroller and business manager. Bob had been doing the books for and giving counsel to C.C.A. for several years, and he saw this as an opportunity to serve his Lord in a greater way. I'm proud to say Bob is my oldest son; he is married to Marsha and has two sons of his own. Bob grew up with the C.C.A. and has been involved in this ministry in one way or another all of his life.

Robert Hultgren

When Bob came on staff, the organization was struggling financially. There were always more places to spend money than there were to get it. He set up a budget and forced the organization to live by it. He was the guiding force and leader in getting the new office building, including arranging for the financing and fundraising. Since he became business manager, the financial status has turned around and the C.C.A. is now on a very sound financial base. Hopefully will have our 3500 square foot office building paid for by the time of our 50th anniversary.

Bob's duties currently include keeping all the financial records, making business decisions, typesetting all newsletters and literature, and running our offset press. He also manages our home office building, keeping all computers and office equipment in working order. Bob truly is the brain that keeps the organization moving in the right direction.

Carolyn Luedtke

Carolyn became C.C.A.'s front office secretary and receptionist in October 1991. Carolyn was a single mother of two teenage children and wanted to work just part-time. It was not long, however, before we realized that her talents were extensive and she was soon handling many of the administrative duties of the association.

Carolyn (Luedtke) Namuth

When Rev. Murphy resigned in 1994, Carolyn was asked to become the C.C.A. Administrator. She was an excellent counselor and soon had many opportunities to counsel members and friends of the association on the telephone. She arranged all of the C.C.A. conventions and set up the clinics for the Salvation Army and the Denver Rescue Mission. She handled almost all of the correspondence and was the heartbeat of the association. Members all over the country love her and remember her exuberant laughter.

In November 2000, Carolyn married Kenneth Namuth. Shortly after, they moved to Eastern Colorado, and Carolyn chose to retire from the C.C.A. Both the members and the rest of the staff truly miss her.

Carla Swihart

On October 1st of 2001, Mrs. Mark (Carla) Swihart joined the staff of the Christian Chiropractors Association. Carla had been office manager for a local Christian school and a chiropractic patient of C.C.A. Member, Dr. Theron Stallings for many years. Carla and Mark have two daughters, Lindsey and Chelsea and are a fine Christian family.

Carla has taken over many of the duties formerly covered by Carolyn in the ad-

Carla Swihart

ministrative capacity of the C.C.A. and has already endeared herself to the Board and members of the organization. Her pleasant voice on the phone, her big smile and her uplifting attitude are a real asset to the home office staff.

Special Members

When I start to mention outstanding members of the Christian Chiropractors Association, I must be aware that it a dangerous thing to do. No matter who we mention, we are bound to leave some one out who also deserves mention. There have been so many members, over the years, who have contributed time, money, and talents to the success of the organization and, who, in other ways exhibited themselves as leaders in the Church and in the profession of chiropractic. This is not meant to memorialize anyone. But special recognition should go to certain ones.

Dr. R. Alvin Niblo

The first one that I wish to mention is Dr. R. Alvin Niblo of Belvidere, Illinois. Dr. Al was one of our quiet members, who was very unassuming but a most brilliant man with many talents. First, he was an engineer before becoming a chiropractor, and used his engineering ability to help in the development of the drop mechanism for the Thompson Terminal Point Adjusting Table. He and Dr. J. Clay Thompson, who got credit for its development, were very good friends and Clay mentioned many times how he would go to Belvidere and pick the brain of Dr. Niblo when he needed help in solving a problem with the drop mechanism.

Dr. Glenn Stillwagon & Dr. R. Alvin Niblo

Secondly, Dr. Al was a professional violinist and played for the Chicago Symphony. This career lasted even into his days as a chiropractor.

Third, Dr. Niblo was a Doctor of Chiropractic who had tremendous confidence in his profession and he exuded it to everyone he met. He had a unique practice which he started every morning at 4:00 a.m. and worked until noon. He also stated that he would go to his office for a couple of hours before patients arrived to do his devotions and study.

Last, Dr. Niblo was a Christian, and not just an ordinary garden variety Christian but a real student of the Bible. He served as Chaplain for the C.C.A. for many years and his teaching was as good as that of any theologian. He was much appreciated by all of our members and he earned the Christian Chiropractor of the Year award in 1966, which was just one small way of showing our appreciation of him.

You might say that if you want to see a Godly man, look for the one who is receiving the most persecution from Satan. It is hard to imagine anyone who suffered more and yet kept such a sweet spirit as that of Dr. Niblo. He and his wife Mary, were involved in a very severe automobile accident, and the injuries they sustained lasted the remainder of their lives. It involved several months in the hospital and in casts and they never would walk normal again. Because of the injuries he received he was unable to bend over his adjusting table so he invented a wall mounted head piece that would enable him to adjust a patients neck while sitting in a chair and leaning against the headpiece on the wall.

A few years later his office was fire bombed and he lost everything - his equipment, his records, his studies and professional notes, and yet he did not loose his desire to continue to serve the Lord and his fellow man. A few years after that, a tornado swept through Belvidere and destroyed much of the City and although his office and home were not destroyed, they did suffer damage. Mary spent the last several years of their married life in a rest home. Dr. Al died in November 1975 at the age of 63 of a sudden heart attack.

Dr. Mattie Carswell Stephens

Dr. Mattie Stephens of Thomaston, Georgia, was one of the original inspirational founders of the Christian Chiropractors Association. (More about her in the Chapter, Founding.)

Dr. Mattie graduated from the Palmer School of Chiropractic in 1936 and one of her classmates was Hazel Kurth, later to become Mrs. Robert N. Thompson. After her graduation, she immediately opened a Chiropractic practice in Thomaston, Georgia and practiced there until her retirement in December 1968. It was her relationship with Dr. Hazel, which inspired Dr. Mattie to want to see an organization of Christian Chiropractors. When Dr. Hazel and Dr. Bob Thompson went to the mission field in the 1940's, Dr. Mattie was one of their faithful supporters. When Dr. Bob asked the profession for help in 1953, to establish a Chiropractic mission to the lepers in Ethiopia, it was Dr. Mattie who accepted the challenge to get that job done.

Dr. Mattie encouraged me, Dr. Glenn M. Hultgren, who at that time was president of the Palmer Student Christian Fellowship Club, to get behind this effort. In the meantime, Dr. Mattie influenced the International Chiropractors Association to start a fund and solicit support for the Thompsons. She served on the Committee to raise the funds, purchase the equipment and get it to Ethiopia. In the mean-

Dr. Mattie Carswell Stephens

time she also prodded me to get the Christians organized and start a Christian Chiropractors Association that the organization might continue the support which she knew the Thompsons would be needing.

Besides her involvement with the C.C.A., Dr. Mattie was very involved in her profession. She was appointed to the Sigma Phi Chi Sorority Advisory Board by its Founder, Dr. Mabel Heath Palmer, and served in that capacity most of her active life. She also was an active member of the International Chiropractors Association.

Dr. Mattie was a faithful servant and witness for her Lord, both in her home Church and in her chosen profession. She died on November 29, 1979 at the age of 81.

Dr. Robert Dryburgh

Dr. Robert Dryburgh graduated from Canadian Memorial Chiropractic College in 1955. After receiving his Doctor of Chiropractic Degree, he and his wife, Joy, moved to London, Ontario where he practiced his profession uninterruptedly for thirty-five years until his untimely death in 1990.

Dr. Bob as an astute Bible scholar and able teacher and preacher of the Word of God. In 1967, he was commended to full-time Christian service by his home assembly, the Hamilton Road

Dr. Robert Dryburgh

Gospel Chapel, a fellowship of the Plymouth Brethren Assemblies of Canada. Dr. Dryburgh was also very active with the Global Outreach Mission Association, serving as its earliest International Director. He later also became a member of the Board of Directors of Global Outreach.

Dr. Dryburgh joined the Christian Chiropractors Association in June of 1965. He had read an article in a Chiropractic magazine about the C.C.A. just two weeks before and, not knowing what kind of an organization it was, he got on a plane and flew to Denver to attend the Annual Convention of the C.C.A. to check it out. His concern was for its spirituality and whether it was developed on a strong Biblical basis. He was more than pleased with what he saw and heard, and became one of its hardest workers and ardent supporters.

Over the years, Dr. Bob served on the C.C.A. Mission Committee, served as Chaplain of the Christian Chiropractors of Canada, and was Keynote Bible Teacher at one of the C.C.A. annual conventions. His strong Biblical teaching and wise counsel, his experience in Mission strategy, was a tremendous help to the Christian Chiropractors Association.

Dr. Lois Baldwin Southern

Dr. Lois Baldwin graduated from National College of Chiropractic in 1949 and went into practice with another doctor in Illinois for several years.

Later she became acquainted with Dr. Chandler Bend who had started a magazine for chiropractic patients called, *The Chiropractic Home*. Dr. Lois became the editor of the magazine, which had a very successful history during the 1950's and 1960's. At first it was published in Illinois and then Dr. Bend and Dr. Lois moved to Brownsville, Texas and published the magazine from there.

Dr. Lois had become a christian in about 1959 and immediately joined the C.C.A. In her capacity as editor of *The Chiropractic Home*, she published many stories about the early work of the C.C.A.

Dr. Lois Baldwin Southern

and became one of its first supporters.

When Dr. Bend lost his health due to age, *The Chiropractic Home* ceased publication and Dr. Lois was without a job. She moved to Houston, Texas and started a practice there as well as started teaching at the Texas Chiropractic College. She had a degree in Nutrition and was a welcome member of the faculty. Dr. Lois joined the C.C.A. in 1959, attended its annual convention in Colorado Springs that year and then served for many years on the Board of Directors of the C.C.A.

Dr. Lois also got involved in a church in Houston and in their singles group met a fine single teacher, who happened to be an outstanding piano player. His name was Phil Southern and it was not long before he and Dr. Lois were married. They never missed attending a C.C.A. Annual Convention and went on many short-term mission trips to Jamaica, Ukraine and other places, as the Lord would lead.

Dr. Lois retired in 1986 and Phil retired shortly after. In 1998, Phil suffered a stroke and their life style changed dramatically from one of very active, to one of dependence. They moved to San Angelo, Texas and Dr. Lois continues to care for Phil who, in spite of his handicap, continues to play the piano, with one hand, and does so much better than most of us will every play with both hands.

Dr. Glenn Stillwagon

Dr. Glenn Stillwagon of Monongahela, Pennsylvania is a man of many talents and tremendous intellectual capacity. He graduated from Palmer School of Chiropractic in 1955, valedictorian in his class. He was a leader in his student class and will also be remembered for his compassion for the less fortunate. He was constant guide and companion to blind student, Jim Westercamp during his student days.

Dr. Glenn Stillwagon

At the first convention of the Christian Chiropractors Association in 1957, Dr. Stillwagon was elected President and he and myself, Dr. Glenn Hultgren, became close friends, companions and co-workers from that day on. The counsel, advice and team work which Dr. Stillwagon provided over the early years for the Association was invaluable to its success. Dr. S. served as President for 14 years and received the Christian Chiropractor of the year award in 1968 for his faithful service to the Association.

In 1968, Dr. Stillwagon, Dr. Harry Kalsbeek and I made our around the world, survey of missions. His leadership ability and his intuitive understanding of situations was of tremendous help to the success of the trip.

Besides Dr. Stillwagon's christian service to the Association and to his church, he had a very creative mind and was constantly finding ways to improve his care of his patients.   In the early days of his practice he invented an analytical instrument called the Derm-o-thermo-graph for recording temperature variations along the spinal column. He was instrumental in developing the Pierce-Stillwagon Adjusting Technique, along with one of his classmates, Dr. Vernon Pierce. This technique was an advanced development of the Thompson Technique, which both doctors had used for several years. After that Dr. Stillwagon and his son, Kevin, invented the computerized infra-red thermography system called the Visi-Therm. This utilized the technology of the computer with infra red sensors for comparative analysis of the peripheral nervous system.

With his many inventions, discoveries and developments in spinal examination, analysis and patient care, Dr. Stillwagon was in great demand as a speaker and teacher at several chiropractic colleges and on many convention programs. Currently his research is ongoing in developing a physiological model for the chiropractic profession. The title of his work will be *"The Neuropathophysiology of the Vertebral Subluxation Complex."*

Dr. Glenn married his wife Lois Marie, soon after his graduation from chiropractic college and they had four sons. Three of the sons became chiropractors. Lois died of cancer in 1991, leaving Dr. Glenn with one of the deepest tragedies of his life. She was his greatest encourager and most enthusiastic supporter. At the age of 77, Dr. Glenn was still practicing his profession and continuing his research in Mononghela, PA when he was struck down by a cerebral hemorrhage on August 16, 2002. He has regained much of his strength and his memory but is not able to return to his work at the time of this writing.

Dr. Willard Smith

After World War II, Willard Smith attended Oklahoma A. & M. (now Oklahoma State University) and graduated in 1949 with a degree in animal science. Before his graduation he was employed by the College to manage their purebred swine farm. Later, he was selected to assist the manager of the college beef operation. He then moved on to teach at Eastern Oklahoma State Technical College. This was a turning point in his life. This was where he met the love of his life, Marguerite, and she introduced him to chiropractic. He had gone to her home to help her because she was in bed with severe back pain, and there Willard met her chiro-

Dr. Willard Smith

practor. Being impressed, when he later developed a migraine headache, he went seeking help from her chiropractor also.

Willard remembers that "my migraine headaches pushed, pulled and pleaded with me to seek health care other than medicine. I could not remember a time from early in my life when I had not been plagued with earaches, headaches, and sometimes backaches." After X-Rays and an adjustment, the pain was gone. However, it did take some time of consistent treatment to stop the headaches completely. But this laid the ground work for Dr. Willard Smith's decision to become a chiropractor.

After he and Marguerite were married in 1954, she encouraged him to attend Palmer College of Chiropractic and he graduated in 1960, a classmate of the two Ethiopian Students. After his graduation Dr. Smith began working in the classroom at Palmer College and remained there for the next forty years. He also maintained a private practice for 39 years in Milan and Rock Island, Illinois.

Dr. Willard has served on the Board of Directors of the Christian Chiropractors Association and also as its President in the early 1970's. He has been the sponsor and counselor for the Christian Chiropractors Student Fellowship for all of his years at Palmer and even after he has retired, he still goes to the College to minister to students. He has made several short-term mission trips, to Bolivia, Haiti and Ethiopia.

His beloved wife and companion, Marguerite, died in 1999 after many years of suffering from ill health. Dr. Willard was her constant friend as well as her loyal helper in her many health problems.

Dr. Kenneth Day

Kenneth Day of Alliance, Ohio, started Palmer College of Chiropractic in late 1955. Almost immediately he joined the student chapter of the C.C.A. and became a Christian in February 1956. Ken was another member who was greatly influenced by Dr. Robert N. Thompson. It was through his contact with Dr. Thompson that Ken became a Christian and immediately he wanted to go into Christian missions. It was Dr. Bob who urged him to complete his chiropractic college first. After his graduation from Palmer in 1959, Dr. Day went to Emmaus Bible College in Oak Park, Illinois to get his

Dr. Kenneth Day

Bible school training and further preparation for the mission field. However, at Emmaus he met the love of his life, Margaret, and they were married in 1960. Margaret was from Stanwood, Washington and she had already completed her training as a Registered Nurse. At that time both of them thought the Lord would lead them into a full time mission ministry.

After their marriage, they returned to Stanwood where Dr. Day set up his chiropractic practice and with family on the way, the decision to go into missions was postponed. Over the next several years, the Days had five children, two, David and Daniel, who would later go on into chiropractic.

During the years that followed, Dr. Day served on the Board of Directors of the C.C.A., on its Missions Board for several years, and as its President in 1976. He also served on the City Council of his city of Stanwood and as its Mayor for 10 years.

His son, Dr. Daniel, joined him in his chiropractic practice in the early 1990's. In April 2000, Dr. Ken suffered a severe debilitating stroke. He spent the next two years in a hospital and rehab center, finally coming home in April 2002. He made good progress at home and was on the road to a degree of physical independence when in July 2002 he had another stroke. This was equally as severe as the first one and he was again sent back to the rehab center. In December of 2002 he again returned home but on a respirator and other life sustaining aids. His mind has remained sound throughout his ordeal and he continues to pray for his family and also for the C.C.A., as they also continue to pray for him. His faithful wife Margaret has been constantly by his side as well as working nights to keep up the insurance needed to continue his care. Dr. Daniel has taken over Dr. Ken's practice and also cares for his father at night while Margaret is working. Although his dream to serve in Christian missions was never realized, Dr. Ken and Margaret Day were very actively involved in the missionary outreach of the Christian Chiropractors Association.

Dr. Fred Vlietstra

Fred was born of parents who emigrated from Holland and settled in northern New Jersey. As a child Fred had epilepsy, the grand mal type. His seizures were severe lasting from 25 to 35 minutes at a time. After going through the usual medical diagnosis and treatment for several years, his parents finally took him to a chiropractor and there Fred got his first relief from his seizures.

As his parents had a dairy farm, Fred learned early in life the value of hard work and working on the dairy was an everyday job for him. Milking the cows, cleaning the barns, putting up hay and all of the other duties associated with a dairy farm were part of Fred's early life.

Dr. Fred Vlietstra

With his memory of the success he had with chiropractic care for his epilepsy, it was natural for Fred to want to follow that career and try to bring help to others who were afflicted as he was. In 1957 Fred left the farm to go to Chiropractic College in Davenport, Iowa. He graduated from the Palmer School of Chiropractic in 1960 in the same class as Dr. Willard Smith and the Ethiopian students, who became good friends of his. After graduation, Dr. Fred returned to Middletown, New York, not too far from the farm on which he was raised and there he set up his chiropractic practice.

He married his childhood sweetheart, Nancy, who was a Registered Nurse and they had one daughter and three sons. Nancy died of cancer at the age of 51 leaving Dr. Fred with four teenage children. In 1994 Fred married Suzanne, who he had known for many years, as they both were involved in the ministry of the Gideons.

Fred was elected President of the Christian Chiropractors Association in 1979 and served that office until 1998. Dr Fred also made many short-term mission trips to Jamaica and two to Africa.

Dr. Douglas Mallett

Dr. Doug Mallett was born and raised on the prairies of Alberta in western Canada. He graduated from Palmer College of Chiropractic in 1975 and set out for a new frontier in eastern Canada. He settled in Newfoundland. He was the first and only chiropractor in that Province and practiced for 17 years before a chiropractic law was enacted. In the first few years he operated four clinics around the Province and drove 2000 miles a month to care for his patients.

Dr. Mallett was instrumental in getting a chiropractic law passed in Newfoundland in 1993 and now reports that

Dr. Doug Mallet

there are between 50 and 60 licensed chiropractors in the Province.

Dr. Doug and his wife are members of strong Bible-based Anglican Church and he has been very involved in their Church, leading over 600 Alpha Course sessions around the area.

Dr. Mallett says his entire life in Newfoundland has been a mission experience, both for chiropractic and for his Christian outreach. He has also been a strong witness for the Christian Chiropractors Association in that part of Canada.

Epilogue

Writing this book was a challenging experience for me. It brought back so many personal memories. As I read over the letters and reports and went through old files (thankfully the staff has kept literally everything), it brought tears to my eyes to re-live all of those events. This book may not have the effect on the readers that it has had on some of us who lived with the people and events recounted here, but I hope that after reading it you, too, will have a better appreciation for what those who went before us went through.

Many of you did not know them personally as I did, and it is hard for me to introduce them to you. For that reason, I have chosen to use what I have called an autobiographical style, whereby each missionary tells his or her own story. I have included many of their letters and reports written at the time of each happening. A more seasoned writer may have done a more professional job, but this is the way I felt I could best convey the message of the 50-year history of our organization.

I hope that you, the readers, have seen that there is a place for chiropractic on the mission fields of the world. Furthermore, I hope you see that it is time for our profession to be included in the full-service health clinics of every mission station.

First of all, this is necessary for the health and well being of the missionary. Too often we hear of a missionary having to come home because of health problems–problems which responded readily to chiropractic care at home. If this service were available on the field, the missionary could have stayed on the field and continued his or her work. Often when the missionary comes home for health reasons, it involves the spouse and family as well, and a whole team is lost.

Secondly, chiropractic can be, and is being, used as a great evangelistic tool. Mission stations have amply proven the fact that a chiropractor can draw more people to the clinic, and treat more patients, than any other profession. Furthermore, the chiropractor can do this with the least amount of expense.

In all fairness to mission societies, we as a profession have not yet demonstrated that there are enough doctors of chiropractic who are qualified and willing to spend their lives for the Lord on some distant mission outpost. This is a sad fact. But as the profession grows, and as the Christian Chiropractors Association continues to promote the idea and challenge its members, more and more doctors are responding to the call.

The next fifty years, if the Lord does not come in the meantime, should be a very different time for the Christian Chiropractors Association and for chiropractic on the mission fields of the world. Cooperation between the medical/dental professions and the chiropractic profession is improving all the time. Cooperation has always been good on the mission field on an individual level, doctor-to-doctor.

As reported throughout this book, the problems, the prejudice, the animosity, and the general opposition to chiropractic on behalf of the medical profession were always instigated by the political arm of the medical profession in North America. In recent years there have been great changes in this regard and much of that opposition has been overcome. I can see a time in the future when complete cooperation is inevitable on the mission fields. This will be great for the total health ministry of missions.

In the early years of the association, our missionary interests were with the full-time missionary. As medical opposition became more severe, our primary emphasis became short-term missionary chiropractors. This involved doctors with little or no theological training, Bible teaching ability, or mission experience, but their enthusiasm and excitement were contagious. The rewards they received for going to a needy field could not be measured in dollars and cents. Many would go year after year. They reported treating hundreds of patients–resident missionaries and nationals as well. Missionaries all over the world praised the efforts of these short-termers and asked them to return.

However, the changing world situation may mean that it is going to be more and more difficult to carry out short-term ministry as we have in the past. I believe that we need to seek more full-time missionary chiropractors, men and women who will dedicate their lives to serving the Lord wherever He calls them to serve. They need to be well trained in their chiropractic skills but also have some Bible training so that they can teach and preach the Word of God as well. In this sense, we may be going back to our beginnings. I believe world situations are going to dictate these changes, and we need to prepare our members–and ourselves–for that change.

In our emphasis on missions, we cannot neglect our ministry to the rank-and-file members at home. The home office staff and the leaders of our organization share a calling to meet the needs of every member. This may involve prayer and counseling when a member is in special need– sickness, death, sorrow, legal problems, divorce, or one of many other problems that are a part of everyday living in this age. Our ministry to our members must never be forgotten. As important as missions is, and in spite of the emphasis which we seem to place upon it, our first calling has to be to the care of our individual members.

Through our C.C.A. members, we want to be a source of spiritual help to the members of our profession at large. No other organization is dedicated to providing spiritual counsel to the members of our profession. Many times when doctors have problems, a malpractice case for example, they can not talk to a pastor or other friend–they can talk to a C.C.A. counselor. We will have the empathy and understanding to deal with those professional issues. We also encourage all of our members to be ready at all times to offer spiritual and Biblical encouragement to non-Christian members of our profession as well.

To the pastors, mission society leaders and Christian laymen reading this book, I do thank you for your interest. I trust that you now have a better understanding of the work of the Christian Chiropractors Association, its mission outreach, and how it is trying to fit into the total picture of Christian missions. I trust also that you will pray more effectively for us as we seek to pray for you and to serve you in Christian ministry. We have a valuable service to provide, and with God's help, we want to use it to His Glory for many years to come.

Glenn M. Hultgren, D.C.

Beginning in 1964, the CCA has recognized a member for outstanding support of and participation in the ministries of the Association. In 1981, it was decided to make a similar presentation to a spouse who is an invaluable asset to his/her chiropractor spouse and demonstrates a commitment to this organization.

Chiropractor of the Year

1964 Dr. Glenn Hultgren
1965 Dr. Hazel Thompson
1966 Dr. R. Alvin Niblo
1967 Dr. Robert Dryburgh
1968 Dr. Glenn Stillwagon
1969 Dr. Harry Kalsbeek
1970 Dr. Willard Smith
1971 Dr. Luther S. Frondal
1972 Dr. James Douglas
1973 Dr. George Wortman
1974 Dr. Henry Esch
1975 Dr. S.G. Wenger
1976 Dr. Kenneth Day
1977 Dr. Fred Vlietstra
1978 Dr. Franklin Torok
1979 Dr. L. Mark Brett
1980 Dr. Al Anderson
1981 Dr. Kenneth Jewell
1982 Dr. Robert Thompson
1983 Dr. James Williams
1984 Dr. Bruce Kniegge
1985 Dr. Lois Southern
1986 Dr. Lester Blank
1987 Dr. Curtis Saunders
1988 Dr. Bruce Hagen
1989 Dr. Appa Anderson
1990 Dr. Daniel Schneider
1991 Dr. Annette Stevko
1992 Dr. Alan Zelm
1993 Dr. Robert Smith
1994 Dr. William Hollensed
1995 Dr. Charles Roost
1996 Dr. Stanley Lindblom
1997 Dr. Chester Smith
1998 Dr. Cecil McLeod
1999 Dr. Richard Black *and* Dr. James Fleming
2000 Dr. Greg Heyart
2001 Dr. Richard Niequist
2002 Dr. Douglas Heise

Spouse of the Year

1981 Mrs. Ruth Wortman
1982 Mrs. Myrtle Anderson
1983 Mr. Phil Southern
1984 Mrs. Marylou Hultgren
1985 Mrs. Katie Kniegge
1986 Mrs. Elsie Jewell
1987 Mrs. Lois Kalsbeek
1988 Mrs. Marguerite Smith
1989 Mrs. Lorena Brett
1990 Mrs. Margaret Day
1991 Mrs. Nancy Vlietstra
1992 Mrs. Barbara Smith
1993 Mrs. Dorothy Williams
1994 Mrs. Phyllis Murphy
1995 Mrs. Beth Hagen
1996 Mrs. Joann Zelm
1997 Mrs. Lorna Hollensed
1998 Mrs. Susanne Vlietstra
1999 Mrs. Dorothy Weber
2000 Mrs. Nancy Smith
2001 Mrs. Marsha Hultgren
2002 Mrs. Susan Scharf

CCA CONVENTIONS

1959 - Colorado Springs, CO
1960 - Toronto, Canada
1961 - Albuquerque, NM
1962 - Davenport, IA
1963 - Lancaster, PA
1964 - Chicago, IL
1965 - Denver, CO
1966 - Tampa, FL
1967 - Dearborne, MI
1968 - Minneapolis, MN
1969 - Louisville, KY
1970 - Toronto, Canada
1971 - Winona Lake, IN
1972 - Estes Park, CO
1973 - Memphis, TN
1974 - Estes Park, CO
1975 - Toronto, Canada
1976 - Anaheim, CA
1977 - Warrington, MO
1978 - Jackson Hole, WY
1979 - Hawaii
1980 - Dearborne, MI
1981 - Los Gatos, CA
1982 - Banff, Canada
1983 - Lancaster, PA
1984 - Breckenridge, CO
1985 - Anchorage, AK
1986 - South Dakota
1987 - Orlando, FL
1988 - Union, WA
1989 - San Diego, CA
1990 - Phoenix, AZ
1991 - Williamsburg, VA
1992 - Estes Park, CO
1993 - San Antonio, TX
1994 - Colorado Springs, CO
1995 - Virginia Beach, VA
1996 - Portland, OR
1997 - Branson, MO
1998 - Sturbridge, MA
1999 - Cheyenne, WY
2000 - Union, WA
2001 - San Antonio, TX
2002 - Hershey, PA
2003 - Fort Collins, CO